We Have a Problem!

Paul Wrangles

Badger
LEARNING

We Have a Problem!

Badger Learning
Suite G08
Business & Technology Centre
Bessemer Drive
Stevenage, Hertfordshire
SG1 2DX

Telephone: 01438 791037
Fax: 01438 791036
www.badgerlearning.co.uk
info@badgerlearning.co.uk

We Have a Problem! Year 6
Paul Wrangles

First published 2012
ISBN 978 1 78147 003 9

Publisher: Susan Ross
Series Editor: Paul Broadbent
Copy Editor: Ursula Faulkner
Illustrations: Paul Wrangles
Text and Cover Design: Cathryn Gilbert

Contents

Introduction

What is 'We Have a Problem!' About?

The short but dull answer to this question is 'it's about helping to teach word problem-solving skills'. A slightly wordier, but far more interesting answer is 'it's about how kung fu, blobs and Mexican waves (amongst other things) can help turn an area of maths that pupils have traditionally found difficult and uninteresting into something more absorbing, challenging and fun!'

This book has useful advice, starter activities, lesson plans, photocopiable resources and a host of creative ideas all aimed at helping teach word problems to a Year 6 class.

These lessons (supplemented by the starter activities), take pupils through the following progression:

1.
Identifying maths usage in real life

Key words
(learn, then use as clues to help identify operation)

Visualising problems
e.g. by doodling and acting out

Picking out relevant/discarding irrelevant information

Splitting multi-step problems into steps

Recognising ambiguities

2.
Solving word problems (strategies)

3.
Creating word problems

Acting out/writing from a given calculation

Writing from an abstract problem

Writing from a given answer

4.
Investigating in real life (i.e. pupil-led enquiry)

In other words, pupils learn the strategies needed to answer teacher-posed questions and eventually use those strategies to answer problems they have come up with themselves.

Before teaching word problems to any class try writing the following two questions on the board.

$$4 \times 6 = \underline{}$$

There are four rockets on the school field waiting to take the class on a trip to the moon.

Each rocket will only hold six people. How many pupils can go on the trip?

Then ask the class which question they prefer to be asked. Here are the three most common replies:

'I don't care. They're both the same.'

'The top one because it tells you exactly what to do.'

'The bottom one. It's more interesting.'

Most children give the second response, but that is not the point here. These replies highlight three important features about word problems:

1. *Word problems are just the same as number questions.*

2. *They're just disguised a bit, that's all.*

3. *Despite the fact that they can sometimes be about the same old topics, word problems have the **potential** to be interesting, relevant and even quite enjoyable.*

And yet, for many children, word problems are not interesting or enjoyable – they're tricky little things. To see through their disguise and pull out the hidden maths needs several skills – skills that have often got nothing to do with numbers. Perhaps a child has difficulties retaining information in their working memory or grasping abstract concepts, i.e. they need to 'see' the actual sum. Maybe they find it hard to apply their knowledge in new contexts or they struggle with reading comprehension. None of these examples are specifically maths-related, but they are integral to solving word problems. If a child struggles with them, they are going to find the subject difficult.

Although good teachers recognise and teach these types of transferable thinking skills, there is no escaping the fact that the maths curriculum still leans heavily towards the solving of algorithms. This is sad because, as 21st century teachers, we are 'preparing students for jobs that don't exist using technologies that haven't been invented in order to solve problems that we don't even know are problems yet' (from *Did You Know V6*, see p.64). Now there's a challenge! The world is changing so rapidly and the using and applying of maths has to keep up.

It's our job as teachers to take the abstract concepts of maths and give children opportunities to use them and see them used – in practical activities, real-life settings, role-play tasks and across the curriculum. It's teachers' role to provide practical experiences out of which pupils can pull out the maths. It's what Foundation Stage and KS1 teachers do all the time, it's what KS2 teachers look for opportunities to do and it's what this resource tries to encourage.

We Have a Problem! will get the class thinking about and dissecting word problems. Hopefully, in amongst the activities, some of the following ideas will be evident.

Remember 'real life' just means life

The term 'real life' seems to be vanishing from the KS2 maths curriculum, which is arguably a good thing. It came to mean anything from 'things that will happen to children when they grow up' (*But, Miss, when will we need this in real life?*) to 'random DIY projects that involve maths', e.g. questions on tiling your swimming pool. Wherever possible, it's important that children are shown that maths is all around them and that it's not just useful when they are adults and are laying carpet. Point out the maths in their lives now. Every time they are splitting into groups; discussing the Premiership table; or counting down the minutes until home time; raise one finger, pause for dramatic effect, and say, 'See? Maths!!'

Hover over their shoulders like some kind of maths genie, they'll soon get the message!

On a serious note, it's impossible to make sure every word problem reflects the life of a Year 6 pupil but, where it *is* possible, show that word problems are as relevant to their life now as they will be when they are tiling that swimming pool.

Keep things as open-ended as possible

We Have a Problem! begins by giving pupils word problems and leading them through some of the strategies they can use to answer them. It ends with pupils coming up with the questions and investigating them. Getting children to lead the way is one of the most exciting (and dangerous!) ways to teach maths. Take a look at some of the links provided on p.63 for ideas in this area.

As well as in investigations, try to pepper word problems with open-ended questions too. For example, instead of asking '*What is the product of 12 and 10?*' rephrase it as '*The product of two numbers is 120. What could the numbers be?*'.

Mixing up question types is crucial

It's so easy to sell pupils short in this regard. Most teachers have done it... After two weeks of division lessons, they wheel out the 'Real-Life Division' worksheet. But, what's the point? Pupils know what's coming. They don't need to understand the question; they just have to divide the numbers. Try it with a class. At the end of a multiplication lesson, ask if they can answer the following...

Mae Alvin yn ysgrifennu cân, ond all e ddim meddwl am ddigon o eiriau.

Mae'n defnyddio 10 o 'oohs' ym mhob cytgan ac mae 8 cytgan yn y gân gyfan.

Faint o 'oohs' sydd yna i gyd?

You don't have to be a fluent Welsh speaker to work out that the answer is 80. Incidentally, the translation is, 'Alvin is writing a song, but he is a bit stuck on the words. He sings 10 "oohs" in every chorus and there are 8 choruses in the whole song. How many "oohs" are there altogether?' However, the answer can be worked out without needing to know the finer details of Alvin's lack of creativity!

In real life, numbers fly at us from all angles. The key skill is knowing what to do with them. Don't give the class a block of multiplication word problems – it won't build that skill.

Initially focus on the question rather than the answer

In order to develop something that is transferable and ultimately of use to children in the real world, it makes sense initially to look to build a skill rather than simply answer a question. In many ways, the *way* pupils reach the solution is much more important than *what* it actually is. Focus more on the *how* than on the *what*. With every word problem from now on, start by telling the class it doesn't matter what the answer is yet – it's more important to know how they will work it out. For pupils who struggle with number work, this takes a load of pressure off immediately. Get hold of a buzzer and read them word problems with bleeped out numbers. Ask the class how they would go about working out the answer. There is a lot of mileage in this little activity.

A slightly different idea is to give the solution straight away. Here is an example. '*Don't worry about the answer... It's 38 chickens! But how do we know it's 38 chickens? What clues are there in the question?*'

Nowhere in this resource is there a discussion on pencil and paper methods for answering problems. Similarly, the important process of estimating an answer, calculating, then evaluating it to check whether it makes sense is hardly mentioned. However, just because these steps are not focussed on, shouldn't mean that they are ignored. There's an answer section at the back (pp.60-62) and, of course, it's important that pupils actually answer and evaluate. But in this particular resource the focus of the lessons and activities is always on **how** pupils would work out the answer, rather than **what** it actually is.

Word problems needn't be boring

Word problems help us with life. Life isn't boring, nor should they be. Over the course of this book, pupils will have opportunities to grapple with word problems – cut them up, act them out and write them down. They'll have worked backwards and forwards to answer them and create them. By the end of the book, they'll have developed a survival kit, a bank of word problems and learned that those key word posters every classroom has are not all they're cracked up to be. This book will show that doodles, kung fu and blobs can all be used to liven up dull word problem lessons.

Remember, interested pupils make the best learners and teachers who can spark that interest make the best teachers. Be sparky!

As 21st-century learners, it's vital that pupils can use and apply the maths they learn, transferring it into different contexts. Developing critical thinking skills is part of this process. In *We Have a Problem!*, the teaching is **through** thinking rather than the explicit teaching **of** thinking.

The skill of ...		... is developed through ...	
	PROCESSING INFORMATION		• identifying the important information in a question • discarding irrelevant information • looking closely at questions to see what they really mean
	REASONING		• justifying a point of view or a strategy adopted • inferring/deducting from key information
	ENQUIRING		• open-ended investigations • breaking down a problem into parts to understand what it is asking
	THINKING CREATIVELY		• predicting possible answers • visualising word problems through doodling • designing own word problems
	EVALUATING		• judging the value of information and ideas • plugging answers back into questions to check they make sense
	DECISION-MAKING		• choosing the most appropriate operation to use • selecting the best strategy to solve a problem

We Have a Problem! will enable teachers to develop these all-important skills in ways that are both interesting and relevant. This isn't an exhaustive resource – please take the ideas within, improve them and build on them. Why not get pupils writing word problems from the point of view of a Roman centurion or in response to *Moonlight Sonata*? What about using cartoons instead of words? Or revising strategies by acting out emergency public service broadcasts for 'What to Do in the Event You Are Attacked by a Word Problem'?

Word problems are tricky little things, but if *We Have a Problem!* inspires teachers to come up with ways to arm their pupils for battle with them, then that can only be a good thing.

The Trouble with Key Words

It is easy to over-emphasise the importance of key words and phrases in deciphering word problems. For example, most classroom walls contain posters stating that a question containing the words 'more than' is an addition question. Of course, for the majority of time it does mean addition as in, 'what is £34 more than £56?'. But those two words could just as easily feature in a subtraction question such as, 'how many more than 92 is 100?'. Or even as part of the story in multiplication or division questions such as, 'Jacob gets paid for helping in the garden and usually earns more than his brother. Last week he earned £12, but this week he earns half that, etc.'

An even more striking example is the word 'add'. Does 'add' always mean 'add'? Think again! 'What would you add to 26 to get 50?' is more easily solved by subtraction than by counting on from 26. In 'Mystery number' questions, the answers are found by doing the opposite to the key words, e.g. 'I think of a number. Multiply it by 20 and I get 60. What was my number?' The word used is 'multiply', but it is actually more useful to divide. This can all get quite confusing for children!

So, although spotting key words and phrases is an important skill, it's nothing compared to

understanding what the question is asking and seeing the key words in that context. Teach key words as clues rather than facts. Clues can be misleading, but every so often they do lead you to the culprit.

When pupils are aware of the ambiguity of key words, the whole subject comes alive. Test the class. Challenge them. Ask them, 'Does it really mean that? Can anyone come up with a question where it would mean something different?'. Instead of having static posters, create something more flexible, e.g. a wall display using post-it notes. Don't just collect key words, collect question types as well. The following table is by no means exhaustive, but here are some key words and key questions that might help.

| **add**
 plus
 total
 altogether
 sum of
 increases
 together
 and
 more than
 perimeter |
 What is __ *added* to __? /*plus* __?
 Add __to__.
 What's the *total* of __ and __?
 __ *and* __, how many *altogether*?
 What is the *sum of* __ and __?
 Which two numbers could have a *sum of* __?
 __ *increases* by __ What is the new amount?
 How much do they weigh *together*?
 __ *and* __ How much *altogether*?
 What is __ *more than* __?
 I think of a number and *subtract* __ I get __. What was my number?
 The sides of a shape are__, what is the *perimeter*?
 Make as many *totals* as you can using any pairs out of __, __, __, __ *and* __. | **subtract**
 difference
 decreases
 minus
 take away
 fewer than
 less than
 how many left? |
 What is __ *subtracted* from __? /*minus* __?
 Subtract __ from __.
 What is the *difference* between __ and __?
 __ *decreases* by __ What is the new amount?
 I have __ and __ are *taken away*. How many *left*?
 What is __ *fewer than* __? /*less than* __?
 How much will I have *left*?
 What number would you *take away* from __ to end up with __?
 How much *longer/shorter* is it?
 How much change will I have?
 How many *less* is __ *than* __?
 Something *added* to __ makes __What is it?
 I think of a number and *add* __ I get __ What was my number? |
| **times**
 multiply
 lots of
 groups of
 total
 altogether
 each in the statement
 twice
 product
 area
 per
 for every
 doubled/ trebled
 perimeter |
 What is __ *times* __?
 What is __ *multiplied by* __?
 What are __ *lots of* __? /*groups of* __?
 __ *groups of* __.What's the *total*?
 __ *lots of* __. How many *altogether*?
 __ people have __ pounds *each*. How much in *total*?
 What is __ *doubled/trebled*?
 What is the *product of* __ and __?
 I think of a number and *divide* by __ I get __. What was my number?
 Is __ a *factor/multiple* of __?
 The length of a rectangle is __ and the width is __.What's the area?
 __ *per/for every* __. How many *altogether*?
 Make as many *products* as you can using the numbers __, __, __ and __. | **shared**
 split
 how many lots/groups?
 split into/ between
 divide
 each in the question
 per
 quotient
 separate
 halved/ quartered
 factors |
 What is __ *shared* between __? /*split* into __?
 How many lots of __? /*groups of* __ are there in __?
 Divide __ by __.
 __ pounds is *split between* __ people. How much will they have each?
 What is the *quotient* of __ and __?
 The area of a shape is __. What could the length and width be?
 How long will it take to save up __ if I save __ *per* week?
 How many different ways can you *separate* __ so that there's the same amount in each pile?
 What are the *factors* of __?
 I think of a number and *multiply by* __ I get __. What was my number? |

Supporting Lower-Ability Pupils

For a lot of pupils, answering word problems is like a bad game of pass-the-parcel. Before arriving at the answer they have to negotiate several heavily sellotaped layers:

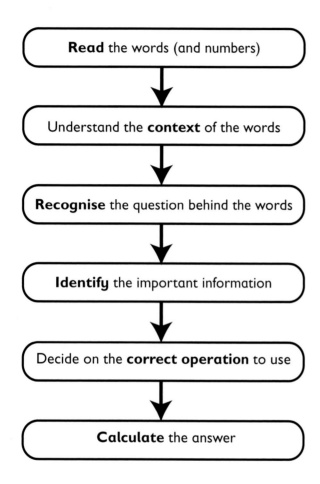

There are some tricky skills there for your lower-ability pupils. And it can leave pupils a little deflated when they eventually reach the grubby, half-melted chocolate bar in the middle of the parcel. *(All that just to find out I had to add them together?)*

Look at a similar list in the context of a word-free calculation...

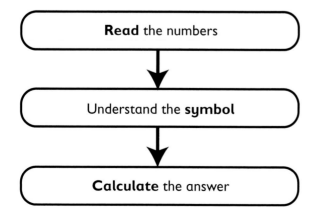

You can see why children might prefer wordless problems! The lesson plans that follow include examples of ways to support pupils who have difficulties with maths, but here are ten general tips to make word problems accessible for them.

Keep your objectives clear

Don't get bogged down in a reading comprehension activity if you want to focus on choosing the correct operation. Concentrate on teaching one skill at a time.

Take the reading aspect away from the task

Give lower-ability pupils a chance to get down to the actual maths by removing reading comprehension barriers to entry. Read problems aloud, record onto tape or use a computer, allowing problems to be heard, not read.

Use illustrations

Pupils derive meaning from illustrations of word problems as with illustrated stories. Seek out illustrated problems in textbooks or collect a bank of suitable photos to accompany problems by doing an Internet image search.

Look for opportunities to use hands-on strategies

Doodle and use real-life objects related to the question as well as things like Cuisenaire rods, plastic cubes, etc. (e.g. *Can you show me the question using real coins?*). This strategy is linked closely to...

Act out problems

Encourage pupils to be the characters in the question and to act out the scenario. This is a great way of helping them to visualise what is going on. *Show me what actually happened here.*

Provide plenty of connections with real-life

Tailor questions to pupils' interests, hobbies, and school topics – anything that helps them build links with the maths.

Use games to reinforce concepts

Use the starter activities on pp.14-27 to build on existing skills/knowledge, then try and turn them into games.

Choose problems with an unknown final quantity

Pupils generally find it easier to work out the answer to questions where the missing answer is at the end. For example, 'Laura has £14, Samantha has £6. How much do they have altogether?' is more straightforward than 'Laura and Samantha have £20 between them. Laura has £14. How much does Samantha have?'.

Encourage pupils to rewrite the problems

Ask pupils, 'Can you put the question in your own words? What if we use simpler numbers?'.

Get pupils to physically dissect the problems

Enlarge copies of problems to enable pupils to cross out/highlight/move around/cut and paste/alter words in the text. Ask them, 'Can you pull out any information we don't need? Where is the key word?'.

Keeping it Relevant

'When am I ever going to need this?' is a question our secondary maths colleagues have to face on a regular basis. To back up pupils' concerns, there is a mildly amusing graph doing the rounds on the Internet showing that the more recently a person has learned something in maths, the more irrelevant it is to real life!

There may be some truth in that, but don't fall into the trap of thinking that every word problem has to be based on shopping or DIY. Yes, word problems are about accumulating knowledge for real-world situations, but they are also about things like problem solving, using logic and evaluating answers. Pupils can learn these skills just as easily through a word problem about the plight of their favourite football team or 'The X Factor' as one about measuring wood.

In fact, it's just as important to be relevant to a Year 6 class as it is to reflect real-world maths. Your word problems need to resonate with them. In his excellent book *Oops! Helping Children Learn Accidentally,* Hywel Roberts emphasises the need to lure a class into learning by gripping them with interesting content, 'if the content is relevant, you may have to work quite hard to make it dull' (from p.51 of Roberts' book). With that in mind, here are six tips for keeping it relevant.

Get to know what makes your class tick

Outside of school, what are their interests? Is your word problem on 'Doctor Who' going to click with them or does it just show how woefully out of

touch their teacher is?! There is no need to pass a questionnaire round – the teachers who know this sort of information are the ones who take the time to chat to their class.

Personalise word problems

Include pupils' names in word problems. Make up far-fetched scenarios that they find themselves in. These may be completely untrue, but if the children in question are good sports they will often play along. Do remember though, that for every child that relishes the limelight there are others who don't want the attention. Know your class.

Write questions based on current events, local or national

Is there anything in the news that is capturing pupils' interest at the moment such as, a sporting event, a local issue or a school trip? Get a handful of newspapers and ask pupils to write word problems based on the issues of the day.

Get pupils to make word problems more relevant

Give them copies of existing word problems (from textbooks/worksheets). Encourage them to use the same numbers and question, but to change the subject matter to something more interesting to them, e.g. a favourite film, famous person or book.

Use humour/the element of surprise

Be creative. Write the sorts of word problems someone like Roald Dahl would have written. If in doubt, remember there is something intrinsically amusing about penguins and chickens!

Build up a bank of word problems

To get the most from *We Have a Problem!*, you're going to need a lot of word problems! Collect together everything your class comes up with during lessons and/or activities by getting pupils to write problems on cards. Categorise them (see pp.56-57), put them in a box and you have a ready-made relevant resource.

Key Word Pyramids

RESOURCES NEEDED:

Sets of *Key Word Cards*
pp.15-17

The following *Key Word Cards* feature a key word or phrase used in word problems (pp.15-17). The final card is a 'joker' (How long?). The answer to this card can be solved by any of the four operations – it provides no clue whatsoever. There is a temptation for pupils to rely solely on what they perceive to be a key word or to expect every word problem to contain one. Including the joker card is a way of showing pupils the ambiguous nature of word problems and should provoke some healthy discussion!

For lower-ability pupils, some of the more difficult key words can be taken out of the pack to allow a focus on some of the more common examples.

ACTIVITY:

➤ Pupils to work in pairs and to be given a set of *Key Word Cards*.

➤ Pupils shuffle the cards, then sort them into piles according to the operation that they refer to.

➤ Within each pile, pupils to sort the cards in order of difficulty (e.g. 'total' is probably a more obvious key word than 'How many altogether?').

➤ Arrange ordered cards in a rough triangle shape (with concepts pupils feel are easier to remember along the wide base and the ones they think are more difficult at the top).

➤ Complete for all four operations.

➤ Compare finished pyramids with other groups. *Why did you put 'What is the product of ___ and ___ ?' at the top of your pyramid? Which key word do you think is the easiest to remember for division?*

➤ The idea of simpler/more difficult key word concepts will be important when pupils design word problems for younger children (see pp.44-45). To preserve these ordered pyramids for use during that lesson, mount onto card or take digital photos.

subtract

multiply

What is __ trebled?

What is ¼ of __?

What is the perimeter?

How many more than __ is __?

What is double __?

The area is __ and the width is __. What is the length?

What is __ halved?

divide

add

minus

total

What is the difference between __ and __?

__ groups of __

shared into

How many altogether?

__ less than __

__ lots of __

split into

What is the sum of __ and __?

How much longer is it?

What are ⅖ of __?

How many will they each have?

How many in all?	What is 30% of __?	__ for every __ (ratio)
fewer	plus	What is the quotient of __?
What is the area?	__ more than __	__ fewer than __
What is the product of __ and __?	How many left?	How long?

Operation Bingo

RESOURCES NEEDED:

Word Problem Cards (pp.19-21)

Sadly, *Operation Bingo* is not a top-secret military codename, it's far more boring than that — it's simply bingo using operations. In order to play, a constant supply of problems is needed, so pp.19-21 contain thirty *Word Problem Cards* to get you started. See pp.56-57 for supplementary questions.

ACTIVITY:

➤ Pupils write four or five operation symbols (out of + − x and ÷) on a piece of paper. They can use them as often or as little as they like and in any order.

➤ Read a selection of word problems from the cards.

➤ If a word problem can be solved by an operation they have chosen, the pupil crosses off the relevant symbol. Bear in mind that some questions can be answered by more than one method, so decide beforehand which to allow.

➤ The winner is the first pupil to cross off all their chosen operation symbols.

DEVELOP IT:

• Play *Extreme Operation Bingo:* the same concept as *Operation Bingo*, but only for the brave. Pupils write down six operation symbols on a piece of paper. Then, instead of reading word problems, pupils have to spot those operations in use around the class over the course of their daily activities. *How long is there until it's home time? Can you split into groups of 3, please?* Under each crossed-out symbol, pupils should record what they spotted.

1.
I think of a number and add 19.
The answer is 83.
What is my number?

2. Hugo Verst, the nervous explorer, goes a quarter of the way into a forest before he gets spooked by a pair of eyes staring back at him.
The forest is 1200m long.
How far did he get?

3.
How many minutes are there in 24 hours?

4.
A kiwi fruit smoothie costs 85p. If you buy one for every day of the week, how much will they cost you?

5.
The length of a rectangle is 14cm.
Its width is 5cm.
What is its area?

6.
Queen Victoria was crowned in 1837 and stayed queen until she died in 1901.
Roughly how long was she queen for?

7.
Six lemon cheesecakes weigh 3000g. How much does 1 cheesecake weigh?

8.
Five times a number is 350.
What is the number?

9.
What is ⅔ of 270?

(CAN YOU SPOT MORE THAN ONE OPERATION?)

10. Last season, Rottenham Wanderers lost 4 times as many games as they won.
They played 35 games.
How many did they win?

(CAN YOU SPOT MORE THAN ONE OPERATION?)

11.

What is the sum of
156 and 258?

12.

Professor Sven Dygram,
the genius mathematician,
says, 'A hundred lots of
my number is 42'.
What is his number?

13. The nervous explorer,
Hugo Verst, is climbing up a
mountain. He starts off at 20m
below sea level and climbs to
10m above sea level.
How high has he climbed?

14.

Name two weights with a
difference of 2.8kg.

15.

What is six-tenths
as a percentage?

16.

How much more is
5298 than 2451?

17. Katy has trained her pet
stick insects to march around
the perimeter of their tank.
The length of the tank is
45cm and the width is 30cm.
How far do they march?

18. In May 2012, a 12 year
old skateboarder won the world
record for spinning 3 times
completely around in one go.
How many degrees did he spin?

19.

Which number, when
multiplied by 1000,
gives you 2300?

(CAN YOU SPOT MORE
THAN ONE OPERATION?)

20.

If everyone in your
class today gave 50p to charity,
how much more would you need
to reach a target of £20?

(CAN YOU SPOT MORE
THAN ONE OPERATION?)

21. A Year 6 teacher goes shopping and buys 'The Big Book of Extremely Hard Maths Tests' for £7.99 and 'How To Get 'Em To Sit Still' for £4.99. How much does she spend in total?

22.

What is the product of 40 and 400?

23.

The average giraffe is about 4.87m tall. How much taller is a giraffe than you?

24.

Two identical cars drive onto a weigh bridge at the same time. The scale says 1800kg. How heavy is each car?

25.

What is the quotient of 63 and 9?

26. Joe wants to go and see the action film 'Beyond the Moon'. The film lasts 80 minutes and finishes at 20:10. What time should he get to the cinema by?

27.

Phoebe spends £8.99 on a book and still has £5.51 left. How much did she have to begin with?

28.

A laptop costs £220 in a half-price sale. How much was it before the sale?

29. To make egg fried rice for 4 people, the recipe says you need 200g of rice. Ryan wants to make it for 6 people. How much rice does he need?

(CAN YOU SPOT MORE THAN ONE OPERATION?)

30. Yasmin thinks of a number, doubles it and then adds 20. The answer is 68. What was her number?

(CAN YOU SPOT MORE THAN ONE OPERATION?)

Doodle It!

RESOURCES NEEDED:

Mini-whiteboards and pens or pencils and paper

Although visualising a word problem is a crucial step along the road to solving it, many pupils find it difficult to conjure up the scene in their head. Using a pencil and paper can help them to 'see' what is being asked and the aim of this activity is to get them to do so.

ACTIVITY:

➢ Read out a word problem (see list below for examples).

➢ *How would you show this problem as a doodle?* Pupils draw the word problem in a way that would help them visualise the question and work out the answer. For example, for the first word problem below, they might might draw a line with crosses to represent each fence post needed.

➢ Encourage pupils to doodle simply and quickly, rather than draw anything too specific. The simpler, the better. Give a time limit to encourage speed.

➢ Share doodles and discuss. If available, use an interactive whiteboard for doodling on. Give different pupils the pen and encourage them to come up with doodles directly on the board. Less confident pupils will benefit greatly from being able to peek at the doodle being drawn by their peers.

SOME WORD PROBLEMS TO DOODLE:

• A farmer is putting up an 18 metre fence. He needs to hammer a fence post in every 2 metres (and at either end). How many fence posts does he need?

• You have a drawer full of socks in four different colours (yellow, green, white and blue). If you don't mind wearing odd socks, how many colour combinations could you make?

• 53 cakes are packed into boxes of 4. Will there be any left over?

DEVELOP IT:

• Do a reversed version of the previous activity. Provide a doodle on the whiteboard. Pupils to work in pairs and suggest possible word problems it could represent.

• Extend the activity further by getting pupils to draw a doodle from suggestions made by the rest of the class.

Kung Fu Problems

RESOURCES NEEDED:

Selection of word problems

Passed down over the centuries, these ancient kung fu moves have led many in the way of the word problem, some becoming great masters of the art.

(*Grateful thanks to Ros Wilson, who originally came up with the idea of using kung fu as a teaching tool, and Phil Beadle, who brought it to the author's attention.*)

ACTIVITY:

1. Teach pupils these all-important kung fu moves, each one representing one of the four operations (noises optional!):

    + Cross forearms to make a plus sign and shout **'PLUS!'**

    − Thrust forearm horizontally to make a minus sign and shout **'MIIIIIIIIII-NUS!'**

    x Cross forearms to make an 'x' and shout **'MULTI-PLIEEEEEEE!'**

    ÷ Thrust left forearm horizontally. Right forearm punches above and below to represent the dots in the sign. Shout **'DEEEEE-VIDE!'**

2. Read a word problem to the class. Pupils respond by performing the corresponding kung fu move.

3. Encourage pupils to think independently — some questions can be answered in different ways. Where there are a variety of methods, pause the activity and discuss why pupils chose their particular operation.

DEVELOP IT:

*   For a faster-paced activity, use key words instead of word problems.

*   Choose a pupil to invent a problem for the rest of the class to perform kung fu moves to.

*   Devise new moves to represent two-step operations.

*   Choose a pair of pupils to perform two kung fu moves at the front of the class. The remainder of the class suggests possible two-step problems they could be representing.

*   Kung Fu Challenge — Split the class into threes. Two pupils face each other and the third is a referee. Pupils respond with kung fu moves to each word problem read out. The winner is the quickest/best performer of the move. Winners play each other until there is one grand master.

*   For the adventurous teacher: instead of kung fu, get pupils to come up with moves for 'Street Dance Maths'. For instance, pupils might suggest a star jump to represent multiplication. How about 'the Caterpillar' for subtraction or 'the Robot' with arms outstretched for addition?! Give it a go.

Mexican Two-Step

RESOURCES NEEDED:

Selection of two-step word problems (pp.56-57)

Mini-whiteboards and pens or pencils and paper

Despite the title, this activity does not involve teaching word problems by way of a little-known Latin dance that you vaguely remember Bruce Forsyth demonstrating once (although there's an idea!). The *Mexican Two-Step* is just a 'show me' activity with a twist. Using mini-whiteboards like this is always an effective way of getting a snapshot of how the whole class answer a question.

ACTIVITY:

➤ Read out a two-step word problem. *William saves £2.50 pocket money a week. After 20 weeks he uses £12.50 of his savings to buy a DVD. How much is left?*

➤ Before moving on, encourage pupils to visualise the problem, look for key word clues, etc.

➤ Pupils to work in pairs and split the question into two parts: 'First, I need to...' and 'Then, I need to...', as in 'First, I need to work out how much William has saved. Then, I need to take off the cost of the DVD.'

➤ Encourage pupils to clarify how they would work out the answer. *Can you doodle it or act it out to help visualise it? Are there any key words that can help you? How would you work out the answer?* (Method: 20 x 2.5 to help find the total of William's savings. Then, subtract 12.5 to work out the amount he has left after buying the DVD).

➤ Pairs write their steps on whiteboards and present them as a mini-Mexican wave!

DEVELOP IT:

• Choose a pair of pupils to decide on two operations and perform a mini-Mexican wave at the front of the class. The remainder of the class then suggest two-step scenarios that could be solved by the operations shown.

• Mexican One-Step: each pupil writes an operation symbol on his or her mini-whiteboard. Read out a word problem. All pupils who think that the question can be solved by using their chosen operation stand up and perform a Mexican wave in their seat!

ICT-Based Activities

The world is changing fast and our curriculum needs to change to reflect the need for more skills-based teaching (ICT is one of those skills, as is problem solving). But there is a difference between using a maths website because it is sparkly and jazzes up the lesson and using it because it furthers pupil learning. Use technology to develop teaching points; not because it's flashy and impressive. This is not an argument against using ICT in maths – far from it. It is just a call to discriminate between the good and the not so good.

The activities below are based on some of the more popular websites (all free to use), although they barely scratch the surface of what is out there. In a quiet moment try one or two of them out (all links, including examples for each website, are on p.63) and ask yourself 'is this sort of thing going to further learning with my class?' If not, no matter how cool the tool, turn the page and move on.

1. Use your interactive whiteboard interactively

It's not just a fancy blackboard! Let pupils explain, demonstrate and show working on your interactive whiteboard more than you do. Take advantage of the way you can move around, highlight, cut and paste word problem text. If appropriate, have children working on the whiteboard during lessons, allowing others to watch and learn with them.

2. Make a bank of images and infographics

Collect images to use to illustrate word problems and as stimuli to get pupils writing their own. Search Internet images using the words 'infographics for kids'. These data-filled images are great for getting pupils to base word problems on.

3. Design interactive posters

Glogster is a tool for creating interactive online posters (Glogs) using text, videos, images and sound. Pupils could make a Glog showing how maths is used in real life. Another idea would be to show 'problem solving strategies' – an online version of the *Word Problem Survival Kit* (pp.26-27). Use finished posters as revision tools with the class.

4. Create key word clouds

Wordle™ generates word clouds from text that users provide. Tagxedo allows you to save the finished word cloud to your computer and you can alter the shape. Pupils can use these tools to create a word cloud containing the key words for a particular operation.

5. Animate word problems

Text-to-animation tools allow users to create short animated films by typing in the text they want characters to say. Get pupils using tools like GoAnimate to create animated word problems for their peers to answer.

6. Have a conversation

The Internet allows a lot of scope for collaborative learning. Wallwisher could be used by pupils to record answers to a word problem or to suggest a word problem based on a given stimulus.

7. Present multi-step problems

Prezi is a zooming presentation tool. Some pupils may need support if creating their own presentations, but it is still useful for demonstration purposes – zooming in on the relevant information and analysing the steps of a multi-step problem.

8. And finally...

An ICT-related tip: most, if not all, keyboards do not have the ÷ symbol. To type it, hold down the ALT key and, using your keyboard's number pad, type the four digits 0, 2, 4 and 7. Let go of the ALT key and ÷ should appear.

Word Problem Survival Kit

Solving word problems is all about becoming familiar with a range of strategies and choosing the right one to fit whatever question is being asked. Some strategies are more common than others (pupils will need to look for key words or doodle more often than they will have to draw a table), but it's important that pupils have a 'go to' base where all the strategies are collected together.

A photocopiable containing the main strategies is provided for pupil use (see opposite), but it is suggested that teachers also set up something more prominent and permanent in the classroom. A *Word Problem Survival Kit* could take the form of a class poster, wall display or a box filled with strategies.

However the survival kit is displayed, it's important that it's referred to regularly in order to embed the strategies pupils need to learn. Point out when strategies have been used by pupils and add new strategies to the kit when they come up in lessons. Rather like a spelling strategy wall or list of class rules, for it to be of any real use, the survival kit should be a constant fixture in the classroom. Its effectiveness is measured by the number of times pupils refer to it.

We Have a Problem! concentrates more on strategies 1–4 than on 5–8 (focussing on the **How?** rather than the **What?**). Be aware of this and encourage pupils to estimate, calculate and evaluate when they reach these stages.

FURTHER IDEAS FOR DEVELOPING THE WORD PROBLEM SURVIVAL KIT:

- Read out a word problem. Pupils choose which tool they could use from the strategies in the kit.

- Provide a strategy, e.g. draw a table. Pupils work in pairs to devise word problems that could be solved using the given strategy.

- Pupils brainstorm objects that could represent the different strategies, e.g. magnifying glass = look for key word clues, marker pen = doodle; then collect the objects to make a survival kit.

- Pupils to design a series of icons representing the different strategies.

- Pupils to act out a public service broadcast giving advice for what to do 'When Word Problems Attack!'

WORD PROBLEM SURVIVAL KIT
(Helping you deal with any word problem emergency!)

Did you know a word problem is just a number sentence in disguise?

These tips will help you to dig deeper and find the number sentence hidden in the words.

1
HIGHLIGHT ANY KEY WORDS

Are there any word or phrases that give you a clue what to do?

2
VISUALISE THE PROBLEM

Can you draw a quick doodle or diagram to help?

3
CIRCLE THE IMPORTANT INFORMATION

What's the important information? What's not?

4
PLAN YOUR STEPS

Can you work out the answer in one go? Or do you need to do more than one step?

5
WRITE OUT THE CALCULATION

Can you write the question as a number sentence?

6
ESTIMATE!

Have you got a rough idea what the answer will look like?

7
CALCULATE!

It's time to work out the answer... Which method are you going to use?

8
EVALUATE!

Look back at the question... Does your answer look right? Have you used the correct units of measurement? Does it make sense?

Real World Maths

PoS/NC LINKS

Pupils should be taught to...

- **Ma2(4a)** choose, use and combine any of the four number operations to solve word problems involving numbers in 'real life'
- **En1(3a)** make contributions relevant to the topic and take turns in discussion

LESSON OBJECTIVES

Pupils will...

- discuss the importance of maths in real-life situations
- identify ways in which maths is used in real life (specifically, in the world of work)
- use key words/phrases (e.g. total, shared between)

RESOURCES

- *Real World Maths* photocopiable

LESSON GROUPINGS

- Whole class introduction
- Individual/paired activity
- Whole class discussion

DIFFERENTIATION OPPORTUNITIES

- Pair pupils in mixed-ability groups for support.
- Choose occupations carefully. Lower-ability pupils may find it easier to consider occupations that have been discussed in class already.

LESSON CONTENT

STARTER: *Operation Bingo* (p.18)

MAIN ACTIVITY: Introduce lesson objective – to identify ways in which maths is used in real life.

Begin by moaning to the class! *What's the point? Why do we need to do maths? When are you ever going to need it?*

Give the DIY example (see p.8). *Is it just people doing DIY and maths teachers who need maths?*

What do we mean by maths? Collect class ideas and ensure some of the less obvious elements are mentioned, e.g. probability, statistics, co-ordinates.

Give pupils a series of real-life scenarios (see below). In pairs, pupils to come up with suggestions as to how maths could help.

- *How could maths help you decide which new car to buy?* (compare fuel consumption, knowing whether to trust the statistics the salesman is giving!)
- *How could maths help you decide how to spend your birthday money?* (calculating how much money you have left after buying several things)
- *How could maths help you win a game show?* (understanding probability/ chance)
- *How could maths stop you from getting lost?* (knowledge of bearing, direction and co-ordinates)

Discuss results as a class.

Now consider jobs. Give the name of an occupation and pupils to come up with maths-related questions that person could ask as part of their job. For example:

- a chef (*How much is 0.1kg flour in grams? How can I change the amounts in this recipe to serve more people?*)
- a pilot (*How high am I flying? How fast do I need to travel to get there on time?*)
- a shop assistant (*Have I given the correct change? Do my accounts balance?*)
- a teacher (*What percentage of pupils were at school today? How long to go until it's home time?!*)

Pupils to complete *Real World Maths* worksheet, choosing an occupation and then coming up with maths-related questions that person could ask.

PLENARY: Pupils then read out their questions and the rest of class have to guess what the occupation is.

Discuss lesson objective as a class. *How is maths used in people's jobs? Which job do you think is the 'mathsiest'?! Why?*

ASSESSMENT OPPORTUNITIES

➢ Do pupils identify uses of maths in real-life?

Name .... Date ....

 Why do we learn maths? Is it useful in real life? Working with a partner, write down six job titles in the table. Then, think of as many maths questions as you can that someone doing that job might ask.

Job	Maths questions they might ask
Mechanic	• How many litres of oil do I need? • What size tyres will fit? • How many miles has the car travelled since the last service?

Which job is the 'mathsiest'? Why do you think this?

Highlighting the Problem

PoS/NC LINKS

Pupils should be taught to...

- **Ma2(4a)** develop further their understanding of the four number operations and the relationships between them including inverses;
- use the related vocabulary; choose suitable number operations to solve a given problem, and recognise similar problems to which they apply
- **En2(3a)** scan texts to find information

LESSON OBJECTIVES

Pupils will...

- recognise key words used in word problems and their ambiguities
- identify the operation needed to solve a word problem

RESOURCES

- *Highlighting the Problem* photocopiables

LESSON GROUPINGS

- Whole class teaching
- Paired/individual whiteboard work
- Individual activity
- Whole class plenary

DIFFERENTIATION OPPORTUNITIES

- Lower-ability pupils to use *Highlighting the Problem 2* as a starting point.

LESSON PREPARATION

Prior to the lesson read through pp.10-11 (The Trouble with Key Words). Teach key words as ambiguous clues, rather than definite facts.

LESSON CONTENT

STARTER: *Kung Fu Problems* (p.23) to revise key words.

MAIN ACTIVITY: Introduce lesson objective – to spot key words in word problems, recognise that they don't always mean the same thing and identify the operation needed to solve them.

Display two questions on the board: '£1.56 x 5 = _____' and 'Abby catches a bus to school every day. It costs her £1.56 per day. How much does it cost per week?'

Emphasise to pupils that you do not really want to know the answer. Instead, you want to think about **how** to solve a word problem.

What do you notice about these questions? Which type of question do you find easier to answer? Why? What makes a good word problem solver? (reading skills, understanding what the question is asking).

Show pupils two more word problems. *Abby's mum gives her £10 every week to pay for her bus tickets. How much money does Abby have left over?* and *Abby has £2.20 left over after spending £7.80 on bus tickets. How much did she have to begin with?*

What do you notice about these questions? (same question slightly rearranged, same key words). *Would you work out the answer in the same way?* (no, the first is a subtraction and the second is an addition question). Explain that key words should be treated as clues rather than facts.

Draw the symbols + − x and ÷ on the board in four sectors. *Can you think of any more key words or phrases that are clues to help you in a word problem?* Pupils work individually or in pairs to brainstorm key word ideas.

Pupils to complete the worksheet *Highlighting the Problem 1* (p.31). Pupils highlight (or underline) the key words and write the operation that could be used to solve the question.

As an extension, pupils to complete *More Highlights!* (p.32). Pupils highlight key words and write calculations (showing ambiguities of key words). Lower-ability pupils to complete *Highlighting the Problem 2* (p.33).

Emphasise that the activity is all about choosing the correct operation (pupils can solve problems, but this should not be lesson focus).

PLENARY: See whether there are any new key words to add to class collection. *Are there any key words that might mean more than one operation?* (altogether, total). *Are key word posters the best way to get children to remember them?*

Give pupils a key word clue and brainstorm possible problems they could write based on it (pupils could continue with the worksheet themes).

ASSESSMENT OPPORTUNITIES

➢ Do pupils identify key word clues in word problems?
➢ Are pupils able to match key words with correct operations?

Name .... Date ....

Each of these questions has got a key word or phrase in it, giving you a clue about how to answer it.

For each question highlight the key words and in each box write the symbol of the operation you would use to find the answer.

1. Trixie-Lou is a celebrity Chihuahua. She is 300mm tall.
The handbag that she is carried around in is 180mm deep.
How much of Trixie-Lou is left poking out of the top?

2. On Wednesdays, Trixie-Lou goes to a pamper parlour.
She starts with a 50-minute shampoo, has a massage for
20 minutes and ends with a 15-minute manicure.
What is the total length of time she spends there?

3. Trixie-Lou doesn't eat just any old dog food, her meals are
prepared daily by her own personal chef. Each day's meals
uses only the finest ingredients and cost £16.45.
How much does her weekly dog food cost altogether?

4. Deep down, Trixie-Lou doesn't like the celebrity lifestyle,
so she decides to rebel. She starts with her owner's socks.
If it takes 3 seconds to chew one sock within an inch of its
life, how many socks can she destroy per minute?

5. The Chihuahua's next target is the luxury white carpet.
Trixie-Lou takes a mud bath outside and then goes for a roll on
the floor. She rolls over 6 times for every metre of carpet in the
12 metre hallway. How many Chihuahua mud-rolls must she do
to wreck it completely?

Name_____ Date_____

You shouldn't rely too much on key words – sometimes they don't mean what you first think they mean. Each pair of questions below has a key word in common, but you have to use different operations to find out the answer.

Highlight the **key words** and then underneath write the calculation you would do to work out the answer. But be careful – things are not always what they seem!

1
a) Nia thinks of a decimal number and doubles it. The answer is 13.6. What was her decimal?

Calculation:

b) Kyle's pocket money is doubled now he is 11. It was £2.45 per week. How much is it now?

Calculation:

2
a) Sacha has £15.30 more than Joe. Joe has £12.80. How much does Sacha have?

Calculation:

b) How many more than 249cm is 925cm?

Calculation:

3
a) How many lots of 500ml are there in 3500ml?

Calculation:

b) What are 53 lots of 22?

Calculation:

4
a) Jordan has £10.25 in his wallet, which is £14.75 less than he started with. How much did he have to start with?

Calculation:

b) What is 8.2kg less than 32.5kg?

Calculation:

5
a) What is the quotient of 864 and 9?

Calculation:

b) The quotient of two numbers is 8. The smaller of the two numbers is 13. What's the other one?

Calculation:

How can two questions have the same key word, but need a different operation to answer them?

Name .... Date ....

Each of these word problems has a key word or phrase in them.
Once you have found each **key word**, highlight it and write a **symbol**
(**+ – x or ÷**) showing how you would work the answer out.

1. Connor's gran is in a band. For her birthday, she'd like a new cardigan for £13, a headband for £2.50 and a pair of drumsticks for £4. How much will the presents cost in total?

2. Gran's band is called 'The Wrinklies'. They have written 29 songs for their new CD, but Gran gets rid of 14 of them because she says they don't rock enough. How many songs are left?

3. Connor's Grandpa doesn't like loud music, so every day he escapes for a walk while 'The Wrinklies' practise in his garage. He walks three miles for every practise. How many miles does he walk per week?

4. At the corner shop, Grandpa stops off for some earplugs. He buys 4 packets and there are 6 earplugs in each packet. How many earplugs does he buy altogether?

5. After a hard afternoon's rocking, 'The Wrinklies' like nothing better than a nice pot of tea and a chocolate biscuit. There are 4 people in the band and they share a plateful of 36 biscuits. How many biscuits do they each have?

You're the Teacher: Which Strategy?

PoS/NC LINKS

Pupils should be taught to...

- **Ma2(4b)** choose and use an appropriate way to calculate and explain their methods and reasoning

LESSON OBJECTIVES

Pupils will...

- explore different strategies for answering word problems
- sort word problems according to answering strategy

RESOURCES

- Set of general word problems (see Lesson Preparation)
- *Which Strategy?* and *You're the Teacher* photocopiables
- Scissors and glue
- Calculators

LESSON GROUPINGS

- Whole class starter
- Paired/Individual activity
- Whole class plenary

DIFFERENTIATION OPPORTUNITIES

- Lower-ability pupils to sort word problems from p.37 (more straightforward problems).

LESSON PREPARATION

Prior to the lesson, it would be useful if pupils were aware of the *Word Problem Survival Kit* (pp.26-27) and that different problems require different strategies..

LESSON CONTENT

STARTER: *Doodle It!* (p.22)

MAIN ACTIVITY: Introduce lesson objective – to sort word problems according to which strategy could be used to solve them.

What strategies could you use to help you answer a word problem? Discuss the *Word Problem Survival Kit* and some of the strategies pupils already use, e.g. doodling, various calculation methods.

Explain that in this lesson pupils will be taking the role of the teacher and sorting out example questions for different strategies.

Write the following strategies on the board: Working Backwards, Writing a List, Trial and Error, and Doodling.

What do you think each of these strategies means? When might you want to use them?

Working Backwards: work from the answer to find one of the starting numbers, usually by reversing any operations already done. Particularly useful for problems that need to find starting number, including 'Mystery number' questions. *I'd saved some money in my piggy bank. Last week I took a quarter of it out and my brother borrowed £3. I now have £33. How much did I have to begin with?*

Writing a List: write down all possibilities, usually using a clear method to make sure all are covered. Particularly useful for questions that ask things like 'how many are possible?' or 'how many different combinations are there?' *How many 2 digit numbers have a 7 or an 8 in them?*

Trial and Error: educated guesswork, often with a calculator – trying an answer and altering it according to how close it is to the target. Particularly useful for questions that are more like number puzzles – finding numbers that fit a certain definition. *Name two consecutive numbers whose product is 156.*

Doodling: drawing something to help visualise a problem. Particularly useful for questions involving shapes, placement of objects and other visual themes. *How many squares are there in a 5 x 5 grid?*

Pupils to complete the worksheet *Which Strategy?* (p.35), sorting questions from pp.36-37 according to the strategy needed to answer them. Lower-ability pupils to complete questions from p.37.

PLENARY: Share answers. Could you answer some questions using more than one strategy? Pupils to work in pairs have a go at answering the problems using the four strategies.

ASSESSMENT OPPORTUNITIES

➢ Do pupils identify correct strategies?

Name.. Date................................

 You're the teacher, but your word problem examples are all mixed up. Can you match the questions with the strategy your pupils should use to solve them?

Working Backwards	**Writing a List**
Trial and Error	**Doodling**

1. Danni thinks of a number, doubles it, then subtracts 32. She ends up with 66. What was her number?

2. Three consecutive two-digit numbers make a total of 138 when you add them together. What are they?

3. How many times does the digit 3 occur in numbers up to 100?

4. Using four straight lines, what's the largest number of slices you can cut a pizza into?

5. How many lines of three in a row can you make on a 4 x 4 grid?

6. Mira spends £23.99 and has £5.51 left. How much did she start with?

7. Using the numbers 6, 7, 8 and 9 in that order, and the signs + – and x in any order, can you make 63?

8. You are allowed to choose 2 sauces in your burger out of a choice of 5: Tomato, BBQ, Spicy, Mayo and Mustard. Which combinations could you pick?

9. There are 5 teams in a league. They play each other twice (home and away). How many matches are there?

10. Two numbers make 480 when you multiply them and 44 when you add them. What are they?

11. Ifzal watches a TV programme for 45 minutes. It ends at 20:05. What time did it begin?

12. There are 6 people in a room. They all shake hands with each other once. How many handshakes are there?

1. Chelsea thinks of a number and doubles it. She ends up with 24. What was her number?

2. Three digits make a total of 24 when you add them together. What are they?

3. Name all the two-digit numbers that have a 9 in them.

4. Using four straight lines, what's the largest number of slices you can cut a pizza into?

5. How many lines of three in a row can you make on a Noughts and Crosses grid?

6. Gemma spends £8 and has £3 left. How much did she start with?

7. Using the numbers 1, 2, 3, and 4 in that order, and the signs + − and x in any order, can you make 1?

8. You are allowed to choose 2 colours for your bedroom out of a choice of 4: Red, Green, Blue and Yellow. Which combinations could you pick?

9. There are 4 teams in a league. They all play each other. How many matches are there?

10. Two numbers make 30 when you multiply them and 11 when you add them. What are they?

11. It takes Cory 10 minutes to walk to school. What time should he leave to get there by 8:40?

12. There are 5 people in a room. They all shake hands with each other once. How many handshakes are there?

Bare Essentials!

PoS/NC LINKS

Pupils should be taught to...

- **Ma2(1b)** identify the information needed to carry out the tasks
- **Ma2(4a)** choose, use and combine any of the four number operations to solve word problems involving numbers in 'real life'

LESSON OBJECTIVES

Pupils will...

- begin to spot the relevant and irrelevant information in a word problem

RESOURCES

- Examples of newspaper headlines
- *Bare Essentials!* photocopiable

LESSON GROUPINGS

- Whole-class teaching
- Individual activity
- Paired plenary

DIFFERENTIATION OPPORTUNITIES

- Lower-ability pupils to be supported/work in pairs.
- Encourage pupils to visualise problems or act out using objects.

LESSON CONTENT

STARTER: Choose a starter from pp.14-27.

MAIN ACTIVITY: Introduce lesson objective – to recognise the important and unimportant (relevant/irrelevant) information in a word problem.

Display a sentence describing a news story. *The Queen adopts a stray ginger cat found in the palace called Charlie.* Discuss the role of a headline writer – to cut the information down to its bare essentials. Which words could a headline writer get rid of to tell the story? Does 'QUEEN ADOPTS STRAY CAT' tell the story still? Revise the terms 'relevant' and 'irrelevant' by looking at examples of headlines.

Display a word problem where the information can be deleted/crossed out (on interactive whiteboard/flipchart). *The Queen buys only the best for Charlie. He wears a diamond-studded collar worth £1500 and his cat food costs £12 per tin. If Charlie eats one tin a day, how much does it cost to feed him for a week?*

Which parts of the word problem are irrelevant? (the first sentence, the price of the collar).

Depending on how the word problem is displayed, physically get rid of the irrelevant information (delete it if on whiteboard, scribble out or rip off if on paper). The physical act of getting rid of the unimportant information should emphasise the need to pull out only the essential facts.

Which pieces of information do you need to work out the answer? (the price of a tin of cat food, the number of tins eaten per day and the question itself). *Circle the relevant information.*

Explain to pupils that in real-life we don't just have the information we need, we have lots extra besides! Give further examples, including problems with irrelevant numerical information.

Pupils to complete *Bare Essentials!* worksheet, rewriting word problems to include only the relevant information.

PLENARY: Give pupils the bare bones of a word problem. *Two items bought at 80p each. How much do they cost altogether?* Pupils to work in pairs, building up the problem by adding irrelevant information.

Pairs to share problems for others to spot the irrelevant information.

ASSESSMENT OPPORTUNITIES

➢ Can pupils identify information as relevant/irrelevant?

Name.. Date..

Sometimes a word problem can seem more like a story than a question.

Read each question carefully, circle the information you think **is** important, cross out all the irrelevant information and write the word problem in the simplest way possible next to it.

1 Alfie is going camping with his family. They start packing the car at 9:30am and set off from home at 10:15am. They arrive at Wettley campsite at 1:35pm. The journey is 200 miles. How long does it take them?

2 Alfie's family are taking 2 tents with them and one car. There are 2 adults and 3 children. They are staying for 3 nights, arriving on Wednesday at 3pm and staying until Saturday at 11am. How much will it cost them to stay there?

> **WETTLEY CAMPSITE**
> "A drop of rain never hurt anybody."
> First tent (including car)   £5 per night
> All extra tents   £3 per night
> Wellington boot hire   £8 daily
> Dry socks (all sizes)   £2.50

3 Alfie is sharing a tent with his brother. Tents are allowed as long as they take up a ground area no bigger than 20m². Alfie's tent is 1.5 metres high, 2 metres wide and 3.5 metres long. What area of the ground will it take up?

4 At 8:30am, after a night spent listening to the wind howl outside the tent, Alfie walks across the wet grass to the shower block. The water is only warm for ¼ of the time and 32 people have washed already. Alfie is in there for 12 minutes. How many minutes is it cold for?

Multi-Step Problems

PoS/NC LINKS

Pupils should be taught to...

- **Ma2(1b)** break down a more complex problem or calculation into simpler steps before attempting a solution; identify the information needed to carry out the tasks

LESSON OBJECTIVES

Pupils will...

- split multi-step problems into separate steps

RESOURCES

- *Multi-Step Problems* photocopiable
- Mini-whiteboards

LESSON GROUPINGS

- Whole class teaching
- Individual/paired activity
- Paired plenary

DIFFERENTIATION OPPORTUNITIES

- Lower-ability pupils to work with two-step problems with addition and subtraction (e.g. objects are added, then taken away, what is the total?) or doubling/halving.

LESSON CONTENT

STARTER: Choose a starter from pp.14-27.

MAIN ACTIVITY: Introduce lesson objective – to spot the steps in multi-step word problems.

Use *Mexican Two-Step* (p.24) as main teaching activity.

Read out a two-step word problem. *Oliver is late for the cinema. It's now 7:15 and the film started 10 minutes ago. The film he wants to see is 1 hour and 35 minutes long. What time will it finish?*

Before moving on, encourage pupils to visualise the problem, look for key word clues, etc.

Pupils to work in pairs and split the question into parts: 'First, I need to... ' and 'Then, I need to... '. *First, I need to find out what time it started. Then, I need to work out the finishing time.*

Encourage pupils to clarify how they would work out the answer. *Can you doodle it or act it out to help visualise it? Are there any key words that can help us? How would you work out the answer?* (take 10 minutes from 7:15pm, then add 1 hour 35 min to the answer).

Pairs to write their steps on whiteboards and present them as a mini-Mexican wave.

Continue with further multi-step examples, including more open-ended questions where the steps are repeated to get various answers.

Class 3 have a Spelling Competition. The winner gets a month off homework. Here are their scores:

	Part 1	Part 2
Amy	34	56
Nia	59	27
William	78	19

Who won the prize? How many points did they get in total?

Pupils to complete *Multi-Step Problems* worksheet, splitting multi-step problems into identifiable parts.

EXTENDED PLENARY: Give class two operations, for example:

Step 1) Multiply
Step 2) Subtract

Pupils to work in pairs and devise multi-step problems to fit the given steps. *Ben saves up his £4 weekly pocket money for 14 weeks. He then dips into his piggy bank to buy his mum a birthday present for £10.50. How much of his savings has he still got left?*

ASSESSMENT OPPORTUNITIES

➤ Can pupils split problems into steps?
➤ Are pupils able to write multi-step problems from a given set of operations?

Name.. Date..

 Sometimes solving word problems involves more than one step. You need to do two or more things to answer each of these questions. Write each step in the boxes underneath.

1. At the Hang Ten Surf Competition, Alicia, Dan and Sophie race each other to the sea carrying their boards. Alicia's time is 20 seconds. Dan beats her by 8 seconds. Sophie takes twice as long as Dan. How long did Sophie take?

Steps needed:

2. Liam hires a surfboard and a wetsuit for an hour and a half. How much change will he get from £25?

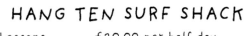

HANG TEN SURF SHACK

Lessons	£20.00 per half day
Surfboards	£8.50 per hour
Bodyboards	£4.00 per hour
Wetsuits	£6.00 per hour

Steps needed:

3. Alicia wants to buy a strawberry smoothie from the Surf Shack because there's a sign saying 'Was 400ml, now 20% larger'. How many millilitres are in the new size?

Steps needed:

4. Dan is standing on the beach giggling at Sophie. He's noticed that Sophie takes 13 seconds to climb onto her board and then in another two seconds she's back in the water! How many times does Sophie fall off in a minute?

Steps needed:

One Way or Another?

PoS/NC LINKS

Pupils should be taught to...

*   **Ma2(1b)** break down a more complex problem into simpler steps; identify the information needed to carry out the tasks
*   **Ma2(1d)** find different ways of approaching a problem in order to overcome any difficulties

LESSON OBJECTIVES

Pupils will...

*   identify possible strategies when answering ambiguous word problems.

RESOURCES

*   *Word Problem Survival Kit* (see pp.26-27)
*   *One Way or Another?* photocopiable

LESSON GROUPINGS

*   Whole class teaching
*   Paired activity
*   Whole-class plenary

DIFFERENTIATION OPPORTUNITIES

*   Lower-ability pupils to work in mixed-ability pairs for peer support. Encourage them to suggest the first method, higher-ability pupil to spot the second.

LESSON CONTENT

STARTER: Choose a starter from pp.14-27.

MAIN ACTIVITY: Introduce lesson objective – to identify and use a range of strategies when answering ambiguous word problems.

Revise what the word 'ambiguous' means and give examples of sentences where the meaning is unclear. *The sticker on the car windscreen reads 'PARKING FINE'. Dog for sale: eats anything and is fond of children.*

Explain that word problems sometimes don't have a key word clue to help you know what to do. Sometimes there's more than one way to work out the answer. Sometimes there's more than one possible answer too!

Display the following word problem. *Carla's dad promises to give her a total of £2 for every 3 times she helps with the washing up. At the end of the month, Carla has earned £16. How many times has she washed up?*

Are there any key word clues in this problem? Is the word 'total' actually a clue? (No, it just refers to the amount Carla's dad gives her.)

So, with no clear key word clues to help, how can you solve the problem? Even though there are no key word clues, visualising the problem can help pupils realise the operation needed is division ($16 \div 3$).

Refer to the *Word Problem Survival Kit* tips (p. 27). Show how looking for key word clues is just one of a series of strategies for solving problems.

Is there another way to solve the problem apart from dividing the numbers? (count up in 3s, subtract 3s from 16).

Provide more examples where pupils can answer in more than one way.

What's 25% of £300? (can be answered by finding 10%, doubling it to get 20%, halving it to get 5% and adding the totals; can also be answered by dividing £300 by 4 to find a quarter). Clearly, one method is a lot quicker than the other.

Most questions can be answered in several ways. Encourage pupils to discuss options, but then to decide on which method they would choose.

Pupils to complete *One Way or Another?* worksheet, suggesting two different methods to work out answers.

PLENARY: Pupils to combine strategies. *Are there any other methods you can think of?* (drawing a table helps with ratio-type questions; drawing a diagram/ working backwards helps with 'Mystery number' type questions). Remind pupils of some of the strategies covered in the *You're the Teacher: Which Strategy?* lesson (p.34).

ASSESSMENT OPPORTUNITIES

➤ Do pupils suggest a range of strategies for solving word problems?

Name_____ Date_____

Not every word problem has a key word to point you in the right direction, but usually there's more than one way to work out the answer. Can you come up with more than one way to work out these problems?

1. Ahmed buys a new laptop. It was £320, but in the sale it's three-quarters of the old price. How much is it now?

One way:	Another way:

2. Ahmed's e-mail inbox can only hold 220 e-mails and at the moment he has 173. How many e-mails before it is full?

One way:	Another way:

3. Ahmed can attach up to 25MB to his e-mail. He wants to send his friend some photos. Each photo is 4MB. How many can he attach?

One way:	Another way:

4. Ahmed is having some problems with his e-mails. For every 3 that send correctly, there are 2 that don't send at all. If he sends 40 e-mails, how many will send and how many will not?

One way:	Another way:

You're the Teacher: Design a Problem

PoS/NC LINKS

Pupils should be taught to...

- **Ma2(4a)** choose, use and combine any of the four number operations to solve word problems
- **En3(1c)** use language and style that are appropriate to the reader

LESSON OBJECTIVES

Pupils will...

- design word problems suitable for younger children
- teach younger children strategies for solving the word problems they have written

RESOURCES

- *You're the Teacher: Design a Problem* photocopiable
- A classful of younger pupils!

LESSON GROUPINGS

- Whole class discussion
- Individual activity
- Whole class plenary
- Paired follow-on activity (with pupils from another class)

DIFFERENTIATION OPPORTUNITIES

- Work in pairs or with support to come up with word problems.

LESSON PREPARATION

Before the lesson, consider which year group would be most suitable to write questions for. The lesson plan below is written with Year 2 in mind, but teachers can adjust according to which year groups are available.

LESSON CONTENT

STARTER: Choose a starter from pp.14-27.

MAIN ACTIVITY: Introduce lesson objective – pupils will be taking on the role of teachers for the lesson, writing word problems suitable for Year 2.

Add value to the activity by giving pupils an audience for their resource. *How could we use your worksheets with other pupils?* (e-mail the word problems to partner schools, use in other year groups, use with future Year 2 pupils).

Explain that although maths are used in real life situations, you can't ususaly pick and choose what numbers you use, but you can in school. *How is a word problem suitable for Year 6 different from one suitable for Year 2?* (different numbers used, vocabulary used is different, scenario relevant to age group, use of multi-step problems). *What sort of subjects should Year 2 word problems be about?* (real-life scenarios relevant to them, familiar stories/fairy tales). Pupils to suggest what sort of calculations are appropriate for Year 2. Write examples.

Pick a calculation and ask pupils to suggest word problems that might fit it. Explore ways in which the wording could change. *Can you find a way to write that without using a key word? Should you keep the numbers fairly simple since you're writing them in a word problem? How could you rewrite that problem so that you only give one of the numbers needed and the pupil has to work the other one out? That's a one-step word problem – how could you make it a two-step problem?*

Pupils to design their own worksheet or set of word problem cards for peers. Use *You're the Teacher: Design a Problem* framework as a class or to support lower-ability pupils.

PLENARY: Hold a teacher training session! Pupils to share some of their word problems and explain. *How would you teach this to a pupil? What strategies would help them understand?* (getting them to visualise it using props, doodling it).

FOLLOW ON:

It's important that these word problem worksheets/cards are actually used by pupils and aren't just displayed or marked and filed away. Some ideas for use are:

- create a Year 2 word problem box to present to their class
- paired sessions with Year 2 pupils
- set up a Wallwisher wall (see p.25) where Year 2 pupils can post their answers to questions.

ASSESSMENT OPPORTUNITIES

- ➢ Can pupils write word problems based on given calculations?
- ➢ Do pupils teach a range of solving strategies to the younger pupils?

Name .... **Date** ....

 Your job is to design some word problems for Year 2 children to answer. Writing questions for younger children needs a lot of skill. Use this framework to help you plan your word problems.

1. Look at the list below and choose the type of maths question you want to base your word problem on.

   Addition and subtraction facts for numbers to 10
   Pairs with totals up to 20 (e.g. 13 + 4, 6 + 14)
   Pairs of multiples of 10 with totals to 100 (e.g. 20 + 30)
   Doubles of numbers to 20 and halves (e.g. 12 x 2, half of 16)
   2, 5 and 10 times tables (and division facts)
   TU – U, TU + U (e.g. 23 + 5, 62 + 3)
   Use m, cm, kg, g, litres and ml
   Read time to the quarter hour (o'clock, quarter past, half past, quarter to)
   Money (adding and subtracting amounts, giving change)

2. Write out a calculation that fits your choice. (e.g. If you use TU – U, you might choose 20 – 7 = 13 to fit.)

3. Cross out one of the numbers (the answer you want people to work out). To make it easier for yourself, cross out the last number. (e.g. 20 – 7 = ~~13~~)

4. Look at the sign. Which key word or phrase could you use to show what sort of a question it is? (e.g. It's a subtraction question so you could make it into a 'how much change' question.)

5. Decide what your question is going to be about. Here are some ideas:

   the time something happens (to the quarter hour)
   two lengths in cm
   the weight of something in grams
   the total amount of money

6. Draft your word problem. (e.g. Joe buys a £7 football. He pays with a £20 note. How much change will he get?)

7. Check it with a partner. Does it make sense?

8. Write it out neatly. (Don't forget to write your answers somewhere so people can mark their work!)

Tricks of the Trade

PoS/NC LINKS

Pupils should be taught to...

- **Ma2(1d)** find different ways of approaching a problem in order to overcome any difficulties
- **Ma2(4a)** choose, use and combine any of the four number operations to solve word problems

LESSON OBJECTIVES

Pupils will...

- understand some of the ways that word problems can catch pupils out

RESOURCES

- Letter from *D. Seaver* (p.47)
- *Tricks of the Trade* photocopiable (p.48)
- *Wanted for Word Problem Trickery!* photocopiable (p.49)
- Past SATs questions with 'tricks' in (e.g. changing units of measurement)

LESSON GROUPINGS

- Whole class teaching
- Individual main activity
- Whole class plenary

DIFFERENTIATION OPPORTUNITIES

- Lower-ability pupils to take existing problems and add irrelevant information or change units of measurement to make them trickier.

LESSON PREPARATION

To hook pupils into the lesson, leave copies of D. Seaver's letter (p.47) lying on pupils' tables before it begins. When they comment on it, make a show of snatching it away and pointing out that it says 'Strictly Not for Children's Eyes!' at the top. Say nothing. Deny everything!

LESSON CONTENT

STARTER: Choose a starter from pp.14-27.

MAIN ACTIVITY: Introduce lesson objective – to understand some of the ways that word problems can catch pupils out.

Grudgingly agree to show pupils the letter. *I've been sent a letter by someone who writes word problems. It's top secret, but I suppose now that you know about it, you might as well read it.*

Circulate copies of D. Seaver's letter (see p. 47) and discuss. Pupils will be using some of his tricks to write their own tricky word problems.

Discuss some of the ways that a word problem writer could 'trick' pupils into making mistakes.

- **give information then change the units of measurement required for the answer**
- **put irrelevant information in**
- **have more than one step**
- **have no obvious key words**
- **don't give all the numbers (get pupils to work it out instead)**

Show pupils examples of past SATs questions. *Can you see what the writer has done here?* (asked for different units of measurement, added irrelevant information, etc.).

Write a simple word problem on the board. *Ryan has £4.50 in his wallet. He buys a can of pop for 65p. How much money does he have left?*

How can we make this trickier? Pupils to use one or two of the tips listed to make the question more difficult. *Ryan has £4.50 in his wallet. £2 of it was given to him by his nan for doing the washing up. He buys a can of pop for 65p and a comic for 99p. How much money does he have now?*

Pupils to complete *Tricks of the Trade* worksheet (p.48), writing their own 'tricky' word problems.

PLENARY: Play 'You Don't Fool Us!' Choose a pupil to read out one of their 'tricky' word problems. The rest of the class write any tricks they can spot on mini-whiteboards. Then, they show their answers to the question writer to prove they're not fooled.

FOLLOW ON: Pupils complete a wanted poster for D. Seaver (p.49), showing the various strategies he uses to make questions trickier.

ASSESSMENT OPPORTUNITIES

➢ Can pupils identify common features of 'tricky' word problems?

Dear Year 6 Teacher,

As the author of most of the tricky word problems used in books, I am writing to you to share some tips to catch your class out with word problems. I'd like to teach you some of the tricks of my trade. There's nothing I like better than trying to fool unsuspecting kids. The only thing I ask is that you don't pass these tips onto them.

I hope that you have a go at trying some of the following techniques in your classroom. Believe me, the children won't suspect a thing and you'll catch them out every single time!

1) CONFUSE THEM WITH MORE THAN ONE THING TO DO

One of my favourite tricks is to write books full of questions where they have to do more than one operation to find the answer.

Here's an example: *Preeta has 34 sweets. She keeps 4 for herself, but decides to share the rest equally amongst 3 of her friends. How many do they each get?*

See what I did there? First, they've got to subtract the 4 and, then, they have to divide by 3.

It's the oldest trick in the book, but it's a good 'un!

2) CHANGE THE UNITS OF MEASUREMENT

Another thing to watch out for is when I change the units of measurement right at the very end of a question. It means they've got to convert the numbers to find the right answer.

For example: *Ben's bookshelf is 120cm high and his computer monitor is 25cm high. How many metres will they be if he puts one on top of the other?*

Did you spot it? Fantastic piece of question design that was… Ask them in 'centimetres' and then BAAM! A 'metres' right at the end! It gets them every time!

3) PROVIDE USELESS INFORMATION

I love using red herrings. Sometimes, I like to ask a question that's so full of irrelevant facts, you can hardly tell where the question is.

For example: *There are four puppies in a rescue centre – Boris, Maurice, Doris and Horace. Horace is half as old as Boris. Doris is a month younger than Maurice. The total of all their ages is 26 months and they have all been at the rescue centre since they were born. Boris has floppy hair and is 6 months old. How old is Horace?*

A beautiful piece of word problem trickery there… The only bits they need to know are the first and last number facts. The rest is unimportant!

There are lots more tricks I use – I hope these help to get you started!

Best wishes,

D Seaver

D. Seaver
Word Problem Author

Name.. Date..

 D. Seaver, the word problem writer, is on the run. In order to catch him, detectives need to see evidence of the sort of thing he is up to.

Below are some simple problems. Rewrite each one showing some of the tricks D. Seaver normally uses to make them tougher. Here are some tricks you might want to use:

- **add more steps to the question**
- **change the units of measurement in the question**
- **give some useless information**
- **give the answer and ask for the starting number (a 'Mystery number' question)**

1 Beth buys a t-shirt for £8 and a pair of sunglasses for £18.
How much does she spend altogether?

2 24 children each donate 50p to charity. How much money do they raise in total?

3 650cm of wire is cut into shorter lengths of 50cm. How many shorter lengths are there?

4 Football matches are 90 minutes long. A football team haven't scored for 10 matches. How long is that without a goal?

Name .... Date ....

 D. Seaver, the word problem writer, is a wanted man. He's guilty of using every trick in the book to fool Year 6 children with word problems.

In the space below, design a 'WANTED' poster, warning the public of some of the devious tricks he uses.

Bloblems!

PoS/NC LINKS

Pupils should be taught to...

- **Ma2(1b)** break down a more complex problem or calculation into simpler steps before attempting a solution; identify the information needed to carry out the tasks
- **Ma2(4d)** recognise, represent and interpret simple number relationships, using formulae in words then symbols

LESSON OBJECTIVES

Pupils will...

- begin to use letters to represent numbers

RESOURCES

- *Bloblems!* photocopiables

LESSON GROUPINGS

- Whole class teaching
- Individual activity
- Whole class plenary

DIFFERENTIATION OPPORTUNITIES

- Encourage pupils to write simple numbers inside the blobs to help visualise the question.

LESSON NOTES

- The *Bloblems!* activities in the previous books (Years 3 to 5) lead up to this point – exchanging blobs for letters as an introduction to algebra.
- It is important that teachers give values to the letters as often as possible. *If q is 10, what will the answer be? If the answer is 20, what's q worth?*

LESSON CONTENT

STARTER: Choose a starter from pp.14-27.

MAIN ACTIVITY: Introduce lesson objectives – to begin to use letters to represent unknown numbers in word problems.

Which letters could we use to represent a number? Are there any letters that we use in maths already? (x symbol for multiplication, p = pence, l = litres). Avoid these at this stage for simplicity.

Draw two blobs (one larger than the other) on the board and the words 'What's the difference?' *Can anyone suggest a word problem that matches this bloblem?*

Show how all the word problems that were suggested were exactly the same (two different numbers and a question).

Show how the problem can be simplified by writing two different letters to represent the two different numbers – what is the difference between *a* and *b*?

What sort of a word problem would this represent? (subtraction of smaller number from larger). *How do you know?* (there are two different numbers, key word clue in the question).

Give values for *a* and *b*. What is the answer?

Show additional examples of bloblems, initially without letters and then with them. Ask pupils to name the operation needed to solve them.

For example:

- *[Four blobs all the same size] How much altogether?* Same expression using letters = 4 x *a*
- *Half of [blob].* Same expression using letters = *a* ÷ 2
- As an extension, try two-step bloblems. For example:
- *[Two blobs of different sizes] How much change will I have from £20?* Same expression using letters = 20 − (*a* + *b*).
- *What's [blob] less than three lots of [blob]?* Same expression using letters = (3 x *a*) − *b*.

Discuss the need to work out the brackets first. Give pupils a silly sentence to help them remember. *And then it makes sense! (Work out the brackets first.)*

Pupils to complete *Bloblems! 1* worksheet (p.51), looking at skeleton problems and choosing which operation is needed.

As an extension, pupils to complete *Bloblems and Letters* (p.52). Lower-ability pupils to complete *Bloblems! 2* (p.53).

PLENARY: Pupils to come to front and invent a word problem. Rest of class to work in pairs and simplify this to a skeleton problem on mini-whiteboards.

ASSESSMENT OPPORTUNITIES

➢ Can pupils use letters instead of numbers in calculations?

Name .... Date ....

 In a bloblem, the blob stands for an unknown number.
Can you work out what these blobs are worth?

1. 124 more than is 9400   =

2. Double  is 732   =

3. £3.50 less than is £8.25   =

4. ¼ of is 90°   =

5. 3 hours split into is 45 minutes   =

 Instead of a blob, you could use a letter.
Can you work out what the letter **q** is worth?

6. The product of 100 and **q** is 320.   **q** =

7. The sum of **q** and 60cm is 1.5m.   **q** =

8. 1kg minus **q** is 780g.   **q** =

9. An hour split into **q** is 20 minutes.   **q** =

10. There are 4 lots of **q** in 2 litres.   **q** =

Name _____ Date _____

 In a bloblem, the blob stands for an unknown number. But you could just as easily use a letter instead of a blob.

Can you match up the bloblems with the correct letter expressions?

1. doubled	**n + q**
2. the difference between and	**n ÷ 2**
3. 10 less than	**2 × n**
4. half of 	**n + 10**
5. the sum of  and	**n − 10**
6. the product of and	**n ÷ 4**
7. 10 more than	**q − n**
8. a quarter of	**n × q**

Name.. **Date**..

 In a bloblem, the blob stands for an unknown number.
Can you work out what these blobs are worth?

1. more than 12 is 20   = ▢

2. Double is 18   = ▢

3. 19 subtract is 15   = ▢

4. split into 3 is 5   = ▢

5. 11 plus is 17   = ▢

 Instead of a blob, you could use a letter.
Can you work out what the letter **q** is worth?

6. **q** more than 5 is 9   **q** = ▢

7. Double **q** is 14   **q** = ▢

8. £12 minus **q** is £7   **q** = ▢

9. **q** split into 10 is 2   **q** = ▢

10. 11 added to **q** is 20   **q** = ▢

Let's Investigate!

PoS/NC LINKS

Pupils should be taught to...

- **Ma2(1b)** break down a more complex problem into simpler steps; identify the information needed to carry out the tasks
- **Ma2(1d)** find different ways of approaching a problem
- **Ma2(1e)** make mental estimates of the answers to calculations; check results

LESSON OBJECTIVES

Pupils will...

- initiate investigations, collect information and write word problems based on their results

RESOURCES

- *Let's Investigate!* photocopiable
- Visual stimuli (see opposite)
- Variety of maths equipment (e.g. rulers, weighing scales)

LESSON GROUPINGS

- Whole-class teaching
- Paired brainstorming activity
- Small group/class investigation
- Whole class plenary

DIFFERENTIATION OPPORTUNITIES

- Encourage lower-ability pupils to choose a question that they can investigate physically (measuring questions are particularly useful).

LESSON NOTES

- Initially, pupils will need teacher direction. This is to be expected. Count it as one step along the road to a completely pupil-led investigation.
- The lesson is completely open-ended, so can be taught over and over using different stimuli.

LESSON CONTENT

STARTER: Choose a starter from pp.14-27.

MAIN ACTIVITY: Introduce lesson objective – to invent word problems from real investigations.

Show pupils a visual stimulus for their investigations. This could be any photo, video or object although it must spark curiosity and be relevant to pupils. Pupils work in pairs to write down as many maths-related questions about the prompt as they can in a spider diagram at the top of the *Let's Investigate!* worksheet. Use question starters on the board.

Collect together all the questions and discuss them. *What information would you need to answer this question? How could you find it out?*

Pupils complete remainder of the planning sheet, deciding on a question to investigate (in groups or as a class). They predict the answer, decide on the information they need to find, collect the necessary information (by measuring, weighing, using the Internet, etc.) and use it to help work out the answer.

After having answered their chosen question, pupils then write a word problem containing the information they found out.

PLENARY: Share results as a class and extend problems to investigate further.

A WORKED EXAMPLE:

1. Show visual stimuli: a chocolate bar and a skipping rope.
2. Collect maths-related questions. *How many chocolate bars would fit along the skipping rope? How much longer is the skipping rope? If you ate the chocolate bar, how much skipping would you have to do to burn off the calories? How many skips are possible in the time it takes to eat a chocolate bar?*
3. Choose question to investigate. *How many chocolate bars would fit along the skipping rope?*
4. Recognise information needed: length of chocolate bar and length of rope.
5. Pupils then measure both items to get correct amounts.
6. Write word problem based on information. *A chocolate bar is 12cm long. How many chocolate bars will fit along a skipping rope that is 1.4m long?*
7. Calculate the answer using mental methods or calculator, depending on complexity.
8. If possible, check answer physically by using the objects themselves.
9. Share results and extend. *How many chocolate bars would fit the length of the playground?*

ASSESSMENT OPPORTUNITIES

- ➤ Do pupils identify the information they need?
- ➤ Can pupils write word problems from real-life investigations?

Name .... Date ....

 Write the name of the prompt in the oval. Then, write down as many maths-related questions as you can around the prompt.

Which question have you chosen to investigate?

Predict what you think the answer could be.

What information do you need to know before you answer the question?

Calculate the answer. Use this space to show your working out...

Now write your investigation as a word problem. Make sure that you include all the information the reader needs to work out the answer.

Word Problems Bank

As has been mentioned several times already, it is crucial to have a bank of word problems to dip into during your teaching. It is also important that these word problems are arranged according to type (rather than operation).

One-step problems (with key words)

1. A rectangle measures 9cm by 21cm. What is its area?

2. Adam's trainers cost £17.50 in a half-price sale. What was their original price?

3. At Grimthorpe Unathletic's last game they had an attendance of 32924. Sadly, Rottenham Wanderers aren't so popular. At their last game, they had an attendance of 4235. How many more people watched Grimthorpe than Rottenham?

4. What is ⅕ of 1.5 litres?

5. Jack buys an MP3 single download costing 72p and an album costing £7.49. How much do they cost altogether?

6. Grace has 2 hours of free calls on her mobile phone. She gets a text message saying 'Time used: 25 mins'. How many minutes does she have left?

7. What is the quotient of 810 and 90? How can you work it out quickly?

8. The temperature today is 7 degrees more than it was yesterday. Yesterday, it was -2°C. What temperature is it today?

9. What is 8 squared?

10. What is £600 as a percentage of £1000?

One-step problems (less obvious working/work backwards)

1. Jessica's bank balance is £150. She pays a bill for £173. What is her balance now?

2. Ashleigh is on holiday in America. The exchange rate is $1 = £0.64. How much is a baseball cap for $10 worth in pounds?

3. An amount added to 800g makes 2.3kg. What is that amount?

4. If Craig's dad drives at an average speed of 60 miles per hour and travels for 2 hours, how many miles can he expect to cover?

5. Anshula thinks of a two-digit number. It's even and its digits make 16 when you add them together. What number is it?

6. How many minutes are there in a day?

7. Caroline's family are going on a 135 mile car journey to the seaside at Skegness. They pass a sign saying 'SKEGNESS 49 MILES'. How far have they travelled?

8. If 0.8 of a pizza has been eaten, what <u>fraction</u> is left?

Multi-step problems

1. In a windsurfing competition, for every 20 seconds Anya stays on her board over 2 minutes, she gets 12 points. She manages to last 5 minutes before falling off. How many points does she get?

2. On the 'SWAPPIT' website people can swap second-hand music for MP3s. A CD is worth 15 MP3s. A vinyl LP is worth 23 MP3s. How many MP3s can you get for 4 CDs and 3 LPs?

3. If you want to convert kilometres into miles roughly, you can take the amount of kilometres, divide it by 8 and then multiply it by 5. Josh is abroad and sees a sign saying 'Paris 32km'. How many miles is that?

4. Charlie's gran is a fan of wine gums. In fact, she takes some of his when he's not looking. Gran sneaks 4 wine gums for every 2 she leaves for Charlie. There are 36 wine gums in a bag. How many will they each have?

5. The cost of a mobile-to-mobile phone call is charged an initial amount of 50p and an extra 20p per minute. You could write this as C = 50 + (20 x m). If Gabby chats on the phone for 10 minutes, how much will it cost?

6. Josh is shopping. One pack of blank CDs costs £4.49, but there is also a special offer where he can buy 3 packs for £11.47. How much will he save by doing the deal?

7. The television programme 'Walking with Llamas' lasts from 6:35pm until 8:05pm. Georgia's mum wants to make a cup of tea exactly halfway through. What time will that be?

8. At the end of Sports Day, Red team have 160 points, Green team have 50 more and Yellow team have double the number of Green team's points. How many points have been scored altogether?

Open-ended/investigational problems

1. Jonathan has a pile of 24 jellybeans in front of him. Just as he's about to tuck in, Callum arrives. They split the sweets equally. How many do they each have? Are there any left over? Then, Jasmin arrives. They split the sweets again. How many do they now each have? Are there any left over? Are there any more numbers of friends that could share the sweets without any being left over?

2. If you started with 1p pocket money every week, and it doubles every week, how long do you think it would take you before you were getting a million pounds a week? Now work it out – double the numbers to find out. Week 1 = 1p, Week 2 = 2p, Week 3 = 4p and so on... After a while, you might like to use a calculator!

3. 'As I was going to St. Ives, I met a man with seven wives.
Each wife had seven sacks.
Each sack had seven cats.
Each cat had seven kits.
Kits, cats, sacks, wives – how many were going to St. Ives?'
After a while, you might like to use a calculator!

4. If you gave every gift in the song 'The Twelve Days of Christmas', how many gifts would your true love have? (On the first day they have a partridge in a pear tree = 1 gift, on the second day they have two turtle doves and a partridge = 3 gifts, etc.)

5. Simon has done some research on a games console he wants to buy. His local shop sells them for £150, a website in America is selling them for $234 and one in Germany is selling them for 185 Euros (postage is free for all of them!). Find out the exchange rates and work out which one is the cheapest. You might want to use a calculator.

6. What's the average shoe size in Year 6? Now, time yourselves running a short distance. Does having bigger feet make you a faster runner?

7. A prime number is a special number. It only has two factors: 1 and itself. How many prime numbers are there between 0 and 30?

8. Steven is playing Extreme Darts. He divides all the numbers around the board by 10 to get decimals. What are the 20 new numbers? Steven throws three darts and gets a total of 4.3. At least one of the darts lands on a double. What could the darts be?

Quick Reference Grid

Starter/Lesson Title	NC Refs	Learning Objectives	Assessment Opportunities	Pages
Key Word Pyramids	Ma2(4a)	Recognise and understand some of the key words used to describe each of the four number operations in word problems. Order the key words from simplest to most difficult.	Do pupils sort key words correctly? Can pupils justify why they've chosen a specific order?	14-17
Operation Bingo	Ma2(4a)	Recognise and understand some of the key words used to describe each of the four number operations in word problems.	Can pupils match word problems with the operation needed to solve them?	18-21
Doodle It!	Ma2(1d)	Use doodles to visually depict word problems.	Can pupils represent word problems visually? Do pupils suggest appropriate word problems to match given doodles?	22
Kung Fu Problems	Ma2(4a)	Identify the operations needed to solve specific word problems.	Visual assessment of pupil responses.	23
Mexican Two-Step	Ma2(1b)	Identify the successive operations needed to solve two-step problems.	Can pupils split problems into two steps?	24
Word Problem Survival Kit	Ma2(1d)	Identify and use a range of strategies when solving word problems.	Do pupils use a range of strategies when answering word problems?	26-27
Real World Maths	Ma2(4a) En1(3a)	Discuss importance of maths in real-life situations. Identify ways in which maths is used in real-life (specifically, in the world of work). Use key words/phrases.	Do pupils identify uses of maths in real-life?	28-29
Highlighting the Problem	Ma2(4a) En2(3a)	Recognise key words used in word problems. Identify the correct operation needed to solve a word problem.	Do pupils identify key word clues in word problems? Are pupils able to match key words with correct operations?	30-33

Starter/Lesson Title	NC Refs	Learning Objectives	Assessment Opportunities	Pages
You're the Teacher: Which Strategy?	Ma2(1b) Ma2(4b)	Explore different strategies for answering word problems. Sort word problems according to answering strategy.	Do pupils identify correct strategies?	34-37
Bare Essentials!	Ma2(1b) Ma2(4a)	Spot the relevant and irrelevant information in a word problem.	Can pupils identify information as relevant/irrelevant?	38-39
Multi-Step Problems	Ma2(1b)	Split multi-step problems into separate steps.	Can pupils split problems into steps? Are pupils able to write multi-step problems from a given set of operations?	40-41
One Way or Another?	Ma2(1b) Ma2(1d)	Identify possible strategies when answering ambiguous word problems.	Do pupils suggest a range of strategies for solving word problems?	42-43
You're the Teacher: Design a Problem	Ma2(4a) En3(1c)	Design word problems suitable for younger children. Teach younger children strategies for solving the word problems they have written.	Can pupils write word problems based on given objectives? Do pupils teach a range of solving strategies to the younger pupils?	44-45
Tricks of the Trade	Ma2(1d) Ma2(4a)	Understand some of the ways that word problems can catch pupils out.	Can pupils identify common features of 'tricky' word problems?	46-49
Bloblems!	Ma2(1b)	Begin to use letters to represent unknown numbers.	Can pupils use letters instead of numbers in calculations?	50-53
Let's Investigate!	Ma2(1b) Ma2(1d) Ma2(1e)	Initiate investigations, collect information and write word problems based on results.	Do pupils identify information they need? Do pupils choose appropriate methods to calculate answers? Can pupils write word problems from real-life investigations?	54-55

Answers

Word Problem Cards pp.19-21

1. $83 - 19 = 64$

2. $1200 \div 4 = 300m$

3. $24 \times 60 = 1440$ minutes

4. $85 \times 7 = 595p$ or £5.95

5. $14 \times 5 = 70cm^2$

6. $1901 - 1837 = 64$ years.
   Her exact reign was slightly less than this as she died early in 1901. She reigned for 63 years, 7 months and 2 days.

7. $3000 \div 6 = 500g$

8. $350 \div 5 = 70$

9. $270 \div 3 = 90$; $90 \times 2 = 180$

10. $35 \div 5 = 7$
    $7 \times 4 = 28$ games lost
    $7 \times 1 = 7$ games won

11. $156 + 258 = 414$

12. $42 \div 100 = 0.42$

13. $-20 + 30 = 10$, so he has climbed 30m

14. Open-ended. Smaller weight subtracted from larger weight must equal 2.8.

15. $0.6 \times 100 = 60\%$

16. $5298 - 2451 = 2847$

17. $45 + 45 + 30 + 30 = 150cm$

18. $360 \times 3 = 1080°$

19. $2300 \div 1000 = 2.3$

20. Open-ended. Multiply class number by £0.50, then take total from £20.

21. $7.99 + 4.99 = £12.98$

22. $40 \times 400 = 16000$

23. Open-ended. Subtract child's height from 4.87.

24. $1800 \div 2 = 900kg$ (apparently this is the rough weight of a 'supermini')

25. $63 \div 9 = 7$

26. $20:10 - 1$ hour 20 mins $= 18:50$

27. $8.99 + 5.51 = £14.50$

28. $220 \times 2 = £440$

29. $200 \div 2 = 100g$ for 2 people
    $100 + 200 = 300g$ for 6 people

30. $68 - 20 = 48$; $48 \div 2 = 24$

Highlighting the Problem 1 p.31

1. how much is left? ($300 - 180$)
   $300 - 180 = 120mm$ of Chihuahua poking out of the top

2. total ($50 + 20 + 15$)
   $50 + 20 + 15 = 85$ minutes $= 1$ hour 25 minutes

3. each/'altogether' in the question (16.45×7)
   $16.45 \times 7 = £115.15$

4. per ($60 \div 3$)
   $60 \div 3 = 20$ chewed-up socks

5. for every (6×12)
   $6 \times 12 = 72$ Chihuahua mud-rolls

More Highlights! p.32

1. doubles/doubled
   a) $13.6 \div 2 = 6.8$
   b) $2.45 \times 2 = £4.90$

2. more than
   a) $15.30 + 12.80 = £28.10$
   b) $925 - 249 = 676cm$

3. lots of
   a) $3500 \div 500 = 7$
   b) $53 \times 22 = 1166$

4. less than
   a) £10.25 + £14.75 = £25.00
   b) $32.5 - 8.2 = 24.3kg$

5. quotient
   a) $864 \div 9 = 96$
   b) $13 \times 8 = 104$ (so, the quotient of 104 and 13 is 8)

Highlighting the Problem 2 p.33

1. in total (+)
   $13.00 + 2.50 + 4.00 = £19.50$

2. how many left? (−)
   $29 - 14 = 15$ songs

3. for every/per (x)
   $3 \times 7 = 21$ miles in a week

4. in each/altogether (x)
   $4 \times 6 = 24$ earplugs

5. share/'each' in the question (÷)
   $36 \div 4 = 9$ biscuits each (very rock and roll)

Which Strategy? p.35

Some questions could be answered in several ways. One way of sorting is as follows (numbering applies to both p.36 and 37):

WORKING BACKWARDS: Questions 1, 6 and 11

WRITING A LIST: Questions 3, 8 and 9

TRIAL AND ERROR: Questions 2, 7 and 10

DOODLING: Questions 4, 5 and 12

You're the Teacher: Which Strategy? 1 p.36

1. $66 + 32 = 98$; $98 \div 2 = 49$

2. $45 + 46 + 47 = 138$

3. 20 times (3, 13, 23, 30, 31, 32, twice in 33, 34, 35, 36, 37, 38, 39, 43, 53, 63, 73, 83 and 93)

4. 12 slices

5. 24 possible lines (two for each row and column = 16, two for each diagonal = 4, plus four extra diagonal lines)

6. $23.99 + 5.51 = £29.50$

7. $6 - 7 + 8 \times 9 = 63$

8. 10 combinations
   (T-B, T-S, T-Ma, T-Mu, B-S, B-Ma, B-Mu, S-Ma, S-Mu, Ma-Mu)

9. 20 matches (1 v 2, 1 v 3, 1 v 4, 1 v 5 and reverse = 8

matches; 2 v 3, 2 v 4, 2 v 5 and reverse = 6 matches; 3 v 4, 3 v 5 and reverse = 4 matches; 4 v 5 and reverse = 2 matches)

10. The numbers are 20 and 24.

11. 20:05 – 45 minutes = 19:20

12. There will be 15 handshakes (this is the fifth triangular number. If there were seven people in the room, the answer would be 21 – the sixth triangular number).

You're the Teacher: Which Strategy? 2 p.37

1. $24 \div 2 = 12$

2. $7 + 8 + 9 = 24$

3. 19, 29, 39, 49, 59, 69, 79, 89, 90, 91, 92, 93, 94, 95, 96, 97, 98 and 99

4. 12 slices

5. 8 possible lines (one for each row and column = 6, and two diagonals)

6. $8 + 3 = £11$

7. $1 \times 2 + 3 - 4 = 1$

8. R – G, R – B, R –Y, G – B, G –Y, B –Y

9. 6 matches (1 v 2, 1 v 3, 1 v 4, 2 v 3, 2 v 4, 3 v 4)

10. The numbers are 5 and 6.

11. 8:40 – 10 minutes = 8:30

12. There will be 10 handshakes (this is the fourth triangular number – see comment above for p.36, q.12)

Bare Essentials! p.39

Open-ended writing activity, although each word problem should include just the necessary information (see below)

1. 10:15 to 1:35pm is 3 hours 20 minutes or 200 minutes
   Relevant information: time of departure (10:15am), time of arrival (1:35pm)

2. 5 x 3 nights = £15 for the first tent and car
   3 x 3 nights = £9 for the second tent
   15 + 9 = £24 altogether
   Relevant information: prices in table, number of tents, number of nights staying

3. $2 \times 3.5 = 7m^2$
   Relevant information: tent length and tent width

4. 12 ÷ 4 = 3 minutes warm
   12 – 3 = 9 minutes cold
   Relevant information: fraction of time it is warm for, how long Alfie is in there for

Multi-Step Problems p.41

1. Step 1: Take 8 seconds from Alicia's time (faster = less time)
   Step 2: Double the result
   20 – 8 = 12 seconds
   12 x 2 = 24 seconds
   So Dan took 12 seconds, Sophie took 24 seconds

2. Step 1: Add £8.50 and £6 to find total for one hour
   Step 2: Find half of the total for half an hour
   Step 3: Add the two together

Step 4: Take the total cost from £25
8.50 + 6 = £14.50
£14.50 ÷ 2 = £7.25
14.50 + 7.25 = £21.75
25 – 21.75 = £3.25 change

3. Step 1: Find 10% of 400 by dividing by 10
   Step 2: Double the amount to find 20%
   Step 3: Add the total to 400ml
   400 ÷ 10 = 40ml
   40 x 2 = 80ml
   400 + 80 = 480ml

4. Step 1: Add 13 and 2 to get 15 seconds altogether
   Step 2: Divide 60 seconds by 15
   13 + 2 = 15 seconds
   60 ÷ 15 = 4 times a minute

One Way or Another? p.43

The following are suggestions for solving the problems – there may be other methods.

1. Find ¼ of the amount (÷4) and take it away from 320.
   Find ¼ of the amount (÷4) and multiply by 3.

2. Start with the smaller and count onwards.
   Subtract the smaller from the larger numbers.

3. Divide 25 by 4 and ignore the remainder.
   Count in 4s until you reach as near to 25 as possible.

4. Draw a table:

SENT	UNSENT	TOTAL
3	2	5
6	4	10
9	6	15 ...and so on

Divide 40 by 5 (because 3 + 2 = 5), then, multiply the answer by 3 to find sent e-mails and 2 to find unsent e-mails.

Tricks of the Trade p.48

Open-ended activity

Bloblems! 1 p.51

1. $9400 – 124 = 9276$

2. $732 \div 2 = 366$

3. $8.25 + 3.50 = £11.75$

4. $90 \times 4 = 360°$

5. $180 minutes \div 45 = 4$

6. $320 \div 100 = 3.2$

7. $150 – 60 = 90cm$

8. $1000 – 780 = 220g$

9. $60 \div 20 = 3$

10. $2000 \div 4 = 500ml$

Bloblems and Letters p. 52

1. A blob doubled = $2 \times n$

2. The difference between a blob and another blob = $q – n$

3. 10 less than a blob = $n – 10$

4. Half of a blob = $n \div 2$
5. The sum of a blob and another blob = $n + q$
6. The product of a blob and another blob = $n \times q$
7. 10 more than a blob = $n + 10$
8. A quarter of a blob = $n \div 4$

Bloblems! 2 p.53
1. $20 - 12 = 8$
2. $18 \div 2 = 9$
3. $19 - 15 = 4$
4. $3 \times 5 = 15$
5. $17 - 11 = 6$
6. $9 - 5 = 4$
7. $14 \div 2 = 7$
8. $12 - 7 = £5$
9. $10 \times 2 = 20$
10. $20 - 11 = 9$

Word Problems Bank p.56
One-step problems (with key words)
1. $9 \times 21 = 189 \text{cm}^2$
2. $17.50 \times 2 = £35.00$
3. $32924 - 4235 = 28,689$ more people
4. $1.5 \div 5 = 0.3$ litres or $1500 \div 5 = 300$ml
5. $0.72 + 7.49 = £8.21$
6. $120 - 25 = 95$ minutes or 1 hour 35 minutes
7. $810 \div 90 = 9$
    A quick way to work this out is to use the number fact $81 \div 9 = 9$ to help.
8. $-2 + 7 = 5°C$
9. $8 \times 8 = 64$
10. $^{600}/_{1000}$ is the same as $^{60}/_{100}$ which equals 60%

One-step problems (less obvious working/work backwards)
1. $150 - 173 = -£23.00$ (£23 overdrawn)
2. $0.64 \times 10 = £6.40$
3. $2300 - 800 = 1500$g or 1.5kg
4. $60 \times 2 = 120$ miles
5. The number is 88.
6. $24 \times 60 = 1440$ minutes
7. $135 - 49 = 86$ miles travelled
8. $1 - 0.8 = 0.2$ As a fraction this is $^2/_{10}$ or $^1/_5$.

Multi-step problems
1. $5 - 2 = 3$ minutes over 2 minutes
    3 minutes = 180 seconds
    $180 \div 20 = 9$; $9 \times 12 = 108$ points
2. $4 \times 15 = 60$ MP3s for 4 CDs
    $3 \times 40 = 120$ MP3s for 3 LPs
    $60 + 120 = 180$ MP3s altogether
3. $32 \div 8 = 4$ $4 \times 5 = 20$ miles
4. $4 + 2 = 6$

$36 \div 6 = 6$
$4 \times 6 = 24$ wine gums for Gran
$2 \times 6 = 12$ wine gums for Charlie

5. $20 \times 10 = 200$
    $50 + 200 = 250$p or £2.50
6. $4.49 \times 3 = £13.47$
    $13.47 - 11.47 = £2$
7. 6:35 until 8:05 is 90 minutes
    $90 \div 2 = 45$ minutes
    $6:35 + 45 = 7:20$pm is halfway through
8. $160 + 50 = 210$ points for Green team
    $210 \times 2 = 420$ points for Yellow team
    $160 + 210 + 420 = 790$ points altogether

Open-ended/investigational problems
1. The pile of 24 jellybeans can be split into 1, 2, 3, 4, 6, 8, 12 and 24 (the factors of 24).
2. After 15 weeks, you would be on a 3-digit amount (£163.84).
    After 18 weeks, you would be on a 4-digit amount (£1310.72).
    And it would take only 28 weeks before you were on £1,342,177.28 a week.
3. The trick answer is one person was going to St. Ives, all the rest were coming back from there. The slightly more taxing answer is...
    $7 \times 7 = 49$ sacks
    $49 \times 7 = 343$ cats
    $343 \times 7 = 2401$ kits
    You + 1 man + 7 wives + 49 sacks + 343 cats + 2401 kits = 2802 going to St. Ives
4. Amazingly, the gifts will total 364. One present for every day of the year except Christmas!
5. Open-ended activity
6. Open-ended activity
7. The prime numbers less than 30 are 2, 3, 5, 7, 11, 13, 17, 19, 23 and 29.
8. Open-ended activity

Houston ... It's We Have A Problem!

Food for Thought

Finding word problems/investigations

Each of the following links will provide you with examples of word problems or investigations. There are plenty more to find, so get searching! Incidentally, it is worth remembering that by including the search terms 'primary', 'KS2' or 'maths', you are limiting yourself to mainly UK-based resources. Don't forget to try 'elementary', 'k–12' (kindergarten to Grade 12) and 'math' too.

http://www.tes.co.uk

http://www.teachingideas.co.uk/maths/contents_problemsolving.html

http://bit.ly/HGfLWordProbs

http://illuminations.nctm.org/

http://nrich.maths.org/public/

http://www.woodlands-junior.kent.sch.uk/maths/wordproblems/index.html

Useful web tools

The following links relate specifically to the websites mentioned on p.25. They are just a tiny selection of the many useful websites out there and examples showing how they can be used. Although many sites encourage you to sign up to a plan, all the examples below were created freely.

Glogster – http://www.glogster.com/   An example: http://bit.ly/GlogsterExample

Wordle™ – http://www.wordle.net/   An example: http://bit.ly/WordleExample

Tagxedo – http://www.tagxedo.com/   An example: http://bit.ly/TagxedoExample

GoAnimate – http://goanimate.com/   An example: http://bit.ly/SavannahProblem

Wallwisher – http://wallwisher.com/   An example: http://bit.ly/SportyWordProblems

Prezi – http://prezi.com/   An example: http://bit.ly/PreziTwoStep

Infographics

Google image search – For example: http://bit.ly/InfographicsForKidsSearch

Pinterest – For example: http://pinterest.com/readingrockets/infographics/

Interesting photos (for teacher use):

National Geographic – http://on.natgeo.com/InspiringPhotos

BBC News in Pictures – http://bbc.in/PhotosOfTheDay

To explore more websites and get ideas of how to use them creatively in your classroom:

- 'Web 2.0' refers to websites where users can generate their own content, so if you perform an Internet search for something like 'web 2.0 classroom resources' or 'web 2.0 tools for teachers' you should get plenty of ideas.

- Join www.twitter.com. If you are not sure how it can help, just think of it as your own PLN. Follow innovative teachers and search for hashtags like #mathchat (maths-based chat), #edtech (using technology in the classroom) or #ukedchat (UK-based teachers).

- If you are ever stuck for classroom inspiration, Pinterest is a great source of ideas. For example: http://pinterest.com/weareteachers/

On teaching word problems

Word problems – connecting language, mathematics and life: http://bit.ly/WordProblemsArticle

Headline stories: http://bit.ly/ThinkmathHeadlineStories

On thinking differently and creative teaching

Oops! Helping Children Learn Accidentally, Hywel Roberts, Independent Thinking Press, 2012

Dancing About Architecture – A Little Book of Creativity, Phil Beadle, Crown House Publishing, 2011

The Sparky Teaching Philosophy

http://bit.ly/SparkyThoughts

On teaching and learning in the 21st century

Why Do I Need A Teacher When I've Got Google? Ian Gilbert, Routledge, 2010

To make you think about where you are going...

http://bit.ly/OECD21stCentury

http://bit.ly/ChangingParadigms

http://bit.ly/DidYouKnowV6

Keep abreast of changes to the KS2 curriculum...

http://www.education.gov.uk/schools/teachingandlearning/curriculum/nationalcurriculum

Real-world maths

Recently, there have been some interesting developments in the area of maths in the real world.

Dan Meyer's excellent TED talk (http://bit.ly/MathsMakeover) discusses the importance of sparking curiosity in pupils. His Three-Act Tasks (http://bit.ly/ThreeActTasks) are for slightly older pupils, but they are well worth mining for real-life investigation ideas.

101 Questions (http://101qs.com/) is a simple site. It displays a photo and asks users to share the first question that comes into their minds (usually maths-related as it is aimed at maths teachers). This is an excellent source of ideas for open-ended investigations that are grounded in the real world.

Mathalicious (http://www.mathalicious.com/) provides lessons based on video clips. At the moment much of the site is subscription-only, but they have received funding to make a bank of videos for teachers to use freely in maths investigations. This is one to keep an eye on.

The author

www.sparkyteaching.com   @SparkyTeaching or the terrible @Ministry_Maths

www.pwillustration.co.uk

The publisher

www.badgerlearning.co.uk   @BadgerLearning